The Schizophrenia Spectrum

About the Authors

Will D. Spaulding, PhD, is a professor of psychology in the doctoral clinical psychology program of the University of Nebraska - Lincoln. His entire career has been devoted to understanding and treating serious mental illness, from psychopathology to treatment outcome to mental health services policy and administration. For over 20 years he was the senior psychologist in a state hospital-based psychiatric rehabilitation program in Nebraska, and has consulted nationally and internationally on development of services for people with schizophrenia spectrum disorders.

Steven M. Silverstein, PhD, is Director of Research, and Director of the Division of Schizophrenia Research at Rutgers University Behavioral Health Care (UBHC), and Professor of Psychiatry at Rutgers - Robert Wood Johnson Medical School. He is the former Chair of the American Psychological Association's Task Force on Serious Mental Illness, and the 2017 President of the Society for Research in Psychopathology. He has over 25 years of experience in treating people with serious mental illness, and has directed inpatient units and outpatient programs for this population. This includes work with both chronically ill and first episode patients. Dr. Silverstein's research interests are in the development of schizophrenia, perceptual and cognitive changes found in schizophrenia, and prediction of treatment response and relapse. He has over 190 publications related to schizophrenia and is currently Principal Investigator (PI) on multiple NIMH or foundation grants involving assessment and treatment. Dr. Silverstein is the recipient of many national and state awards, including the New Jersey Psychological Association's Distinguished Researcher Award in 2009, the American Psychological Foundation Alexander Gralnick Research Award in 2010, and the Trailblazer Award from the Schizophrenia Special Interest Group of the Association for the Advancement of Behavioral and Cognitive Therapy in 2016.

Anthony A. Menditto, PhD, is the Director of Treatment Services at Fulton State Hospital in Missouri. He has spent the past 30 years as a clinician, administrator, researcher, and consultant dedicated to improving our understanding of serious mental disorders. His work has focused on the implementation and evaluation of evidence-based approaches to assessment and treatment for individuals with serious mental disorders.

Advances in Psychotherapy – Evidence-Based Practice

Series Editor
Danny Wedding, PhD, MPH, School of Medicine, American University of Antigua, St. Georges, Antigua

Associate Editors
Larry Beutler, PhD, Professor, Palo Alto University / Pacific Graduate School of Psychology, Palo Alto, CA
Kenneth E. Freedland, PhD, Professor of Psychiatry and Psychology, Washington University School of Medicine, St. Louis, MO
Linda C. Sobell, PhD, ABPP, Professor, Center for Psychological Studies, Nova Southeastern University, Ft. Lauderdale, FL
David A. Wolfe, PhD, RBC Chair in Children's Mental Health, Centre for Addiction and Mental Health, University of Toronto, ON

The basic objective of this series is to provide therapists with practical, evidence-based treatment guidance for the most common disorders seen in clinical practice – and to do so in a reader-friendly manner. Each book in the series is both a compact "how-to" reference on a particular disorder for use by professional clinicians in their daily work and an ideal educational resource for students as well as for practice-oriented continuing education.

The most important feature of the books is that they are practical and easy to use: All are structured similarly and all provide a compact and easy-to-follow guide to all aspects that are relevant in real-life practice. Tables, boxed clinical "pearls," marginal notes, and summary boxes assist orientation, while checklists provide tools for use in daily practice.

The Schizophrenia Spectrum

2nd edition

William D. Spaulding
University of Nebraska-Lincoln, Lincoln, NE

Steven M. Silverstein
Rutgers University Behavioral Health Care (UBHC),
Robert Wood Johnson Medical School, Piscataway Township, NJ

Anthony A. Menditto
Fulton State Hospital, Fulton, MO

Library of Congress Cataloging in Publication information for the print version of this book is available via the Library of Congress Marc Database under the Library of Congress Control Number 2016956064

Library and Archives Canada Cataloguing in Publication

Silverstein, Steven M.
[Schizophrenia]
   The schizophrenia spectrum / William D. Spaulding (University of Nebraska-Lincoln, Lincoln, NE), Steven M. Silverstein (Rutgers University Behavioral Health Care (UBHC), Robert Wood Johnson (Medical School, Piscataway Township, NJ), Anthony A. Menditto (Fulton State Hospital, Fulton, MO). -- 2nd edition.

(Advances in psychotherapy--evidence-based practice ; v. 5)

Revision of: Schizophrenia / Steven M. Silverstein, William D. Spaulding, and Anthony A. Menditto. -- Cambridge, MA ; Toronto : Hogrefe & Huber, ©2006.

Includes bibliographical references.
Issued in print and electronic formats.
ISBN 978-0-88937-504-8 (paperback).--ISBN 978-1-61676-504-0 (pdf).--ISBN 978-1-61334-504-7 (epub)

   1. Schizophrenia--Treatment. 2. Schizophrenia. I. Spaulding, William D. (William Delbert), 1950-, author II. Menditto, Anthony A., author III. Title. IV. Title: Schizophrenia V. Series: Advances in psychotherapy--evidence-based practice ; v. 5

RC514.S544 2016   616.89'8   C2016-906774-2
                                       C2016-906775-0

Cover image © Olivier Tabary/fotolia.com

© 2017 by Hogrefe Publishing
http://www.hogrefe.com

PUBLISHING OFFICES
USA: Hogrefe Publishing Corporation, 7 Bulfinch Place, 2nd floor, Boston, MA 02114
             Phone (866) 823-4726, Fax (617) 354-6875; E-mail customerservice@hogrefe.com
EUROPE: Hogrefe Publishing GmbH, Merkelstr. 3, 37085 Göttingen, Germany
             Phone +49 551 99950-0, Fax +49 551 99950-111; E-mail publishing@hogrefe.com

SALES & DISTRIBUTION
USA: Hogrefe Publishing, Customer Services Department,
             30 Amberwood Parkway, Ashland, OH 44805
             Phone (800) 228-3749, Fax (419) 281-6883; E-mail customerservice@hogrefe.com
UK: Hogrefe Publishing, c/o Marston Book Services Ltd., 160 Eastern Ave.,
             Milton Park, Abingdon, OX14 4SB, UK
             Phone +44 1235 465577, Fax +44 1235 465556; E-mail direct.orders@marston.co.uk
EUROPE: Hogrefe Publishing, Merkelstr. 3, 37085 Göttingen, Germany
             Phone +49 551 99950-0, Fax +49 551 99950-111; E-mail publishing@hogrefe.com

OTHER OFFICES
CANADA: Hogrefe Publishing, 660 Eglinton Ave. East, Suite 119-514, Toronto, Ontario, M4G 2K2
SWITZERLAND: Hogrefe Publishing, Länggass-Strasse 76, CH-3000 Bern 9

Hogrefe Publishing
Incorporated and registered in the Commonwealth of Massachusetts, USA, and in Göttingen, Lower Saxony, Germany

Printed and bound in the USA

ISBN 978-0-88937-504-8 (print) • ISBN 978-1-61676-504-0 (PDF) • ISBN 978-1-61334-504-7 (EPUB)
http://doi.org/10.1027/00504-000

Preface to the Second Edition

The intent of this book is to provide an overview of current conceptualizations of, and treatments for, schizophrenia spectrum disorders. There is an emphasis on psychological treatments. These interventions are usually neglected in graduate and medical training about schizophrenia, even though the evidence for their effectiveness is comparable to that of pharmacologic treatment, with the combination of the two typically producing the best treatment outcomes. However, schizophrenia spectrum disorders are complex conditions with expressions at all levels of a person's biological, psychological, and social functioning. Modern treatment incorporates, integrates, and coordinates modalities that operate at all those levels. Pharmacological treatment addresses the neurophysiological level of the disorders and some of the direct cognitive and behavioral consequences, but this is just one part of the picture. We hope to provide the reader a reasonably complete overall picture of assessment, treatment, and rehabilitation.

Since the first edition, the major developments that required the most attention for the second are:

1. Publication of the fifth edition of the American Psychiatric Association's *Diagnostic and Statistical Manual of Mental Disorders* (DSM-5). The fifth edition introduces the *schizophrenia spectrum* and *neurodevelopmental disorders*, reflecting advances in our scientific understanding of mental illness in general and schizophrenia in particular;
2. Evolution of the idea of *recovery* as central to treatment and rehabilitation, and to the subjective experience of the person affected;
3. Advances in the psychopathology of schizophrenia and other disorders that transform our basic understanding of mental illness as non-categorical, multidimensional processes with indistinct boundaries and multiple interacting etiological factors that are inseparable from the process of human development;
4. A proliferation of psychological and psychosocial modalities for treatment and rehabilitation and their subsequent consolidation into the integrated multimodal arrays and organizational models that characterize modern psychiatric rehabilitation;
5. The continuing failure to disseminate, implement, and effectively regulate modern treatment and rehabilitation methods in our mental health service systems, despite overwhelming evidence for improving outcomes.

We hope this book is useful to a wide range of people, from students first learning about the schizophrenia spectrum to advanced clinicians and researchers looking for a compact review of current conceptualizations and clinical tools. The schizophrenia spectrum represents one of the greatest scientific challenges of our time and also one of the most disenfranchised, undertreated populations in our society. Our hope is that this book will inspire all readers to address the social, political, and humanitarian issues as well as the scientific ones.

Acknowledgments

The authors would like to thank Danny Wedding for providing the opportunity to write this book and for his guidance during the writing process. Will Spaulding would like to thank Rue Cromwell and the late Gordon Paul for guiding his early work in schizophrenia and all the teachers and mentors named by this volume's co-authors, and Mary Sullivan for ongoing love, support, and teamwork. Steve Silverstein would like to thank his mentors and teachers who taught him about schizophrenia and its treatment, including Ray Knight, Michael Raulin, Frank Miller, Jim Bowman, Robert Liberman, Chuck Wallace, and Rich Hunter. He would also like to thank his parents and Judy Thompson for their love and support. Anthony Menditto adds his thanks to Gordon Paul for his pioneering work that laid the groundwork for applying rigorous standards of practice to developing services and properly evaluating them for individuals with severe mental disorders, and for the personal support and guidance he has provided to each of us over the years. He would also like to thank Lynn Geeson and Theresa Menditto for their love and support. All the authors wish to thank all the students from whom we have learned, and, most especially, the people we've been privileged to accompany on their journeys of recovery. We also thank the Hogrefe editorial and production staff for their helpful and professional collaboration and assistance.

Contents

1

Description

1.1 Terminology

1.1.1 Schizophrenia as a Mental Health Policy Construct

Schizophrenia refers to a type of severe and disabling mental illness that affects between .5% and 1.5% of the population worldwide, with a current global prevalence calculated at over 20 million people. It is typically first recognized in late adolescence or early adulthood, and is often associated with lifelong disability, especially when appropriate services are not provided. It has been estimated that as many as ten percent of all disabled persons in the US are diagnosed with schizophrenia.

Schizophrenia affects over 20 million people around the world

Schizophrenia is a specific psychiatric diagnosis, but for the purposes of social policy and healthcare administration it is often grouped together with schizoaffective disorder, bipolar disorder, severe chronic depression, and sometimes other conditions. Such grouping is convenient because treatment and service needs are similar within the group. The diagnoses usually grouped with schizophrenia have in common an onset in late adolescence or adulthood, an *episodic course* (periods of better and poorer functioning), a high risk of severe disability, and in most cases (traditionally) a lifelong need for treatment and support services.

Psychiatric Disability

Psychiatric disability resulting from schizophrenia extends to multiple domains of personal and social functioning. People with the diagnosis are vulnerable to institutionalization, to being found legally incompetent and requiring a guardian, and to needing assisted living situations. As a group they have very high unemployment and poor quality of life. The economic costs of schizophrenia, including direct treatment costs and lost productivity, are enormous (Insel, 2008), among the highest of all health conditions, ranking with cancer and heart disease. The diagnosis accounts for 75% of all mental health expenditures and approximately 40% of all Medicaid reimbursements, although the greatest part of the economic burden comes not from treatment but from the *disability*, i.e., from the lost productivity of those affected (Insel, 2008).

Serious Mental Illness

The term *serious mental illness* (SMI) has been in use for several decades, especially in federal mental health policy, to refer to schizophrenia and the other diagnoses with which it is usually grouped. However, in recent years the meaning of SMI has generalized to include less disabling conditions, sometimes virtually any psychiatric diagnosis (Satel & Torrey, 2016). This would not be a problem if the criteria were sensitive to the actual, measurable degree of *disability*, but in practice expansion of the meaning of SMI directs resources away from those in most need. This issue is related to the so-called practice of "cherry picking," strategically selecting healthcare clients to optimize corporate or individual profits. It is a matter of ongoing concern and debate in the healthcare industry and the mental health policy communities.

The Schizophrenia Spectrum

Schizophrenia spectrum is also used as a group term, although its specific meaning is variable. In the recently issued fifth edition of the American Psychiatric Association's *Diagnostic and Statistical Manual* (American Psychiatric Association, 2013), "Schizophrenia Spectrum," is a sub-family that includes schizophrenia and related diagnoses under the major heading "Schizophrenia Spectrum and Other Psychotic Disorders." DSM-5 also includes *schizotypal personality disorder* in its definition of the schizophrenia spectrum, even though it is placed under the major heading "Personality Disorders." In the scientific literature, "schizophrenia spectrum" is used more broadly, in recognition of the indistinct boundaries of "schizophrenia" as a diagnostic category, the multiple causes and expressions of psychopathology related by common genes, symptoms and other features, and commonalities in treatment. *Schizotypal traits* and other developmental vulnerabilities are considered part of the schizophrenia spectrum whether or not they meet diagnostic criteria for any disorder. For the purposes of this book, the scientific usage of "schizophrenia spectrum" provides a better reflection of its meaning than the DSM usage.

The DSM-5 now classifies schizophrenia as a spectrum disorder

Psychosis

Psychosis is a clinical term that has significant policy implications as well. It is not a diagnosis, but is closely associated with schizophrenia and related diagnoses, sometimes collectively termed *psychotic disorders*. Psychosis is a state often loosely described as detachment from reality, expressed as specific psychiatric symptoms including hallucinations, delusions (expression of unrealistic or bizarre beliefs), disruption of coherent thought and language, and affect inappropriate to the situation (e.g., euphoria in the face of deteriorating personal circumstances, extreme anger without a discernable cause). Sometimes affective symptoms may have associated *psychotic features*, e.g., if depressed mood is accompanied by delusions of guilt. In such cases the psychotic features are said to be *mood-congruent*. Psychosis may be continuous or episodic and is highly variable in quality and severity across individuals and within individuals over time. The presence of psychosis in any clinical picture is indicative of increased morbidity, risk, and disability. Even in the general population, the presence of psychotic symptoms is associated with greater social disability (Rossler et al., 2015) and an increased risk for violent behavior (Silverstein, Del Pozzo, Roché, Boyle, & Miskimen, 2015). Unfortunately, mental health policies, regulations, and practices often fail to recognize and manage the highly variable and episodic nature of psychosis and the individual differences this creates.

Treatment Refractory Schizophrenia

It may seem curious that the term *treatment refractory* appears in a discussion of policy terminology. In fact, the concept behind the term has a pervasive influence on policy and in organization and administration of mental health services. Applied in mental health in the context of severe, disabling disorders, treatment refractory means *refractory to drug treatment*, specifically to treatment with first-generation antipsychotic drugs (see Section 4.1.2). There is no scientific rationale for distinguishing a group based on response to drugs, much less on response to a specific sub-family of drugs. There are, however, commercial and economic reasons to make the distinction, but these are not typically reasons that serve the best interests of consumers. For example, this distinction is often used to support the use of cheaper post-patent medications, to promote prescription of newer, more profitable drugs, or to promote the interests of the medical services industry.

Arguably "treatment refractory schizophrenia" is a terminological relic of the *deinstitionalization* era, the 1970s and 1980s, when the population of psychiatric institutions was dramatically reduced. Policy during that era showed a naïve (in retrospect) expectation that antipsychotic drugs would enable people discharged from the psychiatric institutions to function normally in their communities. Being "refractory" in this context could render the community inaccessible to the person so labeled.

Most people with schizophrenia spectrum disorders are "refractory" to some degree, in the sense that very few people experience complete remission of all aspects of the disorder from drug treatment alone. Most people who are "refractory" to first-generation antipsychotics are responsive to a range of psychological treatments and social interventions, some to a very extensive degree (Newbill, Paul, Menditto, Springer, & Mehta, 2011; Paul & Lentz, 1977; Silverstein et al., 2006; Spaulding, Johnson, Nolting, & Collins, 2012).

1.1.2   Schizophrenia as a Psychiatric Diagnosis

The modern diagnosis of schizophrenia has its origins in the work of Emil Kraepelin, who named it *dementia praecox*, "early dementia." In the early 20th century the Swiss psychiatrist Eugen Bleuler introduced the term "schizophrenia" as he challenged the presumptions underlying Kraepelin's "dementia praecox." "Dementia" is inappropriate, Bleuler argued, because many people recover in ways inconsistent with an irreversible progressive brain disease. Bleuler also argued that the extensive individual differences between people with the same diagnosis suggest that it is not a single disorder, but a group of similar but distinct disorders. He argued that the most important characteristic of the disorder is not its onset or course, but the nature of its expression, particularly in the domain of human functioning we recognize today as *cognition*. He therefore proposed "schizophrenia," derived from Greek for "severed mind" (skhizein, σχίζειν, "to split;" phren, φρήν, "mind") to reflect a fragmentation of mental functioning, including a split between thinking and feeling. Later, misunderstanding of "schiz-" led to the unfortunate and totally erroneous confusion of schizophrenia with "split personality" in popular culture.

> **Schizophrenia was originally labeled *dementia praecox***

> **Schizophrenia does not refer to a split personality, although this is a popular misconception**

Later in the 20th century Bleuler's "schizophrenia" became the accepted diagnostic term in psychiatry, but the key clinical features that comprise the criteria for making the diagnosis were mostly those described by Kraepelin. Scientific debate continued throughout the century about which symptoms are most essential and whether there are subcategories of symptoms reflecting subtypes of schizophrenia. Kraepelin's original subgroups of symptoms gradually evolved into the diagnostic subcategories familiar today: paranoid, hebephrenic, catatonic, and undifferentiated. Two of the original subgroups became *schizoaffective disorder* and *catatonia*, today considered separate diagnoses, not subtypes, but still within the schizophrenia spectrum if not caused by other medical conditions or substance abuse.

In the 1970s a group of academic psychiatrists who became known as "neo-Kraepelinians" gained control of the American Psychiatric Association's *Diagnostic and Statistical Manual of Mental Disorders* (Kutchins & Kirk, 1997). The neo-Kraepelinian agenda was, among other things, to eliminate the influence of psychoanalysis in psychiatry and replace it with an understanding of mental illness as the expression of distinct medical conditions comparable to infectious diseases. Mental illness was reduced to a "broken brain" (Andreasen, 1984). Treatment was not treatment unless it was medical, i.e., pharmacological (Klein, 1980). In 1980 the neo-Kraepelinians issued the 3rd edition of the DSM, which asserted this perspective. "Correct" diagnosis of specific psychiatric diseases, based on observation and patient report of specific symptoms, became a keystone of both research and clinical practice.

The DSM-III was influenced by Emil Kraepelin's original diagnostic system and biological assumptions

The neo-Kraepelinians dominated two editions of DSM, the third (including a revision in 1987) and the fourth, in 1994. By the turn of the 21st century, however, the flaws in such a reductionist approach were no longer manageable. Psychopharmacology contributed importantly to illumination of the flaws, ironically so, because the neo-Kraepelinians expected that drug effects would play a major role in validating their diagnostic system. In fact, the expected correspondence of drug families to diagnostic groups did not develop. By the 21st century, antipsychotic drugs were being used to treat affective and personality disorders, antidepressants were being used to treat anxiety disorders, and mood stabilizers were being used to treat psychosis. Similarly, as behavioral neuroscience matured, the hypothesis that psychiatric disorders are separate diseases caused by distinct genes or pathogens following simple etiological pathways became untenable. It became clear that the population of "people with schizophrenia," as rigorously diagnosed with neo-Kraepelinian criteria, is immensely heterogeneous, as is their response to drugs. The irony is compounded by recent historical scholarship that indicates that by the end of his life Kraepelin himself had come to doubt the validity of his system, in ways that eerily anticipate developments in psychopathology and neuroscience nearly a century later (Engstrom & Kendler, 2015). Had he lived until 1975, Kraepelin probably would not have been a neo-Kraepelinian.

In 2013 the fifth edition of the DSM (DSM-5) was issued. Overall, the reductionist perspective of the previous editions was significantly moderated. Mental illnesses, including schizophrenia, were recognized to be not specific diseases or even distinct categories, but prototypes, "fuzzy sets" with indistinct boundaries and multiple etiologies. The subtypes of schizophrenia were eliminated, based on lack of scientific validation. These changes bring the diagnosis of schizophrenia into better congruence with science, but after decades of research based on neo-Kraepelinian assumptions there will inevitably need to be further changes in how we understand the relationship between science, diagnosis, and practice. Even the youngest readers of this book will see the lingering effects of the neo-Kraepelinian era and of biological reductionism in general in the foreseeable future. The most unfortunate part of this legacy may be expectations for outcome, because the neo-Kraepelinian perspective does tend to reduce schizophrenia to an incurable neurological disease.

Another significant change in the DSM-5 was introduction of the idea of *neurodevelopmental disorders*. As will be discussed in more detail in Chapter 2, the etiological processes associated with the schizophrenia spectrum have come to be recognized as essentially developmental. The DSM-5 defines a new family, "Neurodevelopmental Disorders," that includes intellectual disability (formerly mental retardation), autism spectrum disorders, attention deficit hyperactivity disorder, and other congenital conditions. Schizophrenia was not placed in this family, arguably because disorders manifest at birth or in early childhood need their own category (in DSM's III and IV there was literally a category of *disorders usually diagnosed in infancy, childhood or adolescence*). The schizophrenia spectrum has many *premorbid* manifestations, i.e., abnormalities present before all diagnostic criteria are met, that can be observed as early as infancy in some cases, but the modal window for *onset*, i.e., the point at which *all* diagnostic criteria are met, extends from late adolescence through the early 20s. In recognition of the onset difference, in DSM-5 schizophrenia spectrum disorders are placed just adjacent to the child onset family, in "Schizophrenia Spectrum and Other Psychotic Disorders." Despite being in a separate DSM family, there is strong consensus across the scientific community that the schizophrenia spectrum has neurodevelopmental etiologies.

Most researchers believe schizophrenia spectrum disorders have neurodevelopmental etiologies

In a sense, identifying the onset of a neurodevelopmental disorder is inevitably arbitrary. Many people have serious impairments in their personal and social functioning long before they meet criteria for a schizophrenia spectrum disorder. For some, there is a sudden change of functioning and appearance of psychosis. For others, there is no distinct point of onset, and changes in functioning occur throughout adolescence. This is historically termed an *insidious onset*. The *prodrome*, or condition preceding the actual meeting of full diagnostic criteria, is sometimes so pronounced and protracted that a separate diagnosis for it has been proposed and included in DSM-5 as "attenuated psychosis syndrome," not as a diagnosis but as a condition for further study. There is increasing interest in intervening upon detection of the earliest manifestations of abnormality. Waiting until the onset of psychosis to intervene has been likened to waiting until the patient has a heart attack before diagnosing heart disease.

Similarly, the idea of schizotypy has taken on additional meaning. In addition to representing a developmental vulnerability, *schizotypal personality disorder* is considered a separate diagnosis. This reflects recognition that some of the features of schizotypy, e.g., anhedonia (reduced ability to experience pleasure), magical thinking (illogical reasoning, odd beliefs), and social isolation, can have maladaptive impact independent of the vulnerability to psychosis.

1.1.3   Dimensions of the Schizophrenia Spectrum

Symptom Categories

In contrast to the diagnostic subtypes of schizophrenia, some categorizations of specific clinical features have gained scientific validation and practical value. As long as we do not forget that schizophrenia itself is not really a valid category, other categorical and quantitative dimensions of severe psychopathology can have scientific and clinical utility. We can expect that these types of measures will play an important role in both research and practice in the foreseeable future.

An important example, derived from the work of the 19th century British neurologist John Hughlings-Jackson on neurologic disorders, is the distinction between positive, negative, and disorganized symptoms. *Positive symptoms* are behaviors or experiences not present in the normal population, e.g., the familiar psychiatric symptoms, hallucinations, and delusions. *Negative symptoms* are ones that represent an *absence* of a normal behavior or experience, e.g., a reduced ability to experience pleasure, reduced motivation, blunted affect. Negative symptoms are sometimes further classified as primary or secondary. Primary negative symptoms are those that directly reflect a disease process, whereas secondary symptoms are those that are due to other factors, e.g., social withdrawal secondary to paranoia. *Disorganized symptoms* refer to a fragmentation and breakdown of psychological functions needed to organize behavior for specific purposes (e.g., disrupted thought or speech, purposeless motor activity).

> **Patients with schizophrenia spectrum disorders can present with positive or negative symptoms**

Although grouping of symptoms is categorical, the symptoms themselves can be quantitatively measured. This is important because quantitative measures like symptom severity are usually more useful than categorical distinctions in assessing treatment effects and other outcomes. The significance of the categorical distinctions is whether they identify different situations or people who behave in a distinctive way. For example, there is some evidence that persistently high levels of negative symptoms identify a distinct grouping, termed the *deficit syndrome*, with distinct etiology and treatment needs. However, so far there is very little evidence of categorical differences in treatment needs among people with schizophrenia spectrum disorders.

Psychopharmacological as well as psychological treatment approaches have become primarily focused on individual symptoms rather than symptom categories. However, in general, negative symptoms are generally less responsive to medication than are positive symptoms, although psychological interventions (e.g., activity scheduling, behavioral activation) have been shown to be effective. Patients with high levels of *disorganized* symptoms generally respond least well to antipsychotic medication and to psychological treatment (although specific treatments for this symptom dimension have not been developed), and tend to have poorer long-term outcomes.

> **Patients who present with disorganization as a symptom have a poorer prognosis**

Alternative Views of Psychiatric Symptoms

In an alternative conceptualization of the symptoms of the schizophrenia spectrum, rooted in phenomenology, symptoms are not seen solely as additions to or deletions from normal functioning (Sass & Parnas, 2003). In contrast to the Hughlings-Jackson view, and consistent with many patient self-reports, this perspective recognizes that negative symptoms may not be true deficits, but rather compensatory responses of an individual to *excessive* internal activity. Similarly, positive symptoms such as delusions are not viewed simply as "added on" mental experiences. They are active attempts by a person to make sense of anomalous sensory experiences and to adapt to the many psychological and social implications of being "mentally ill." A classical idea in experimental psychopathology (e.g., Maher, 1988), this explanation continues to be supported by recent research (e.g., Nordgaard & Parnas, 2014).

In the social learning theory perspective, symptoms are social behavior and as such may be expected to acquire instrumental value and become components of social role performance like any other. They may acquire *functional autonomy* from neurophysiological origins, meaning that behavior originally driven by neurophysiological dysregulation in acute psychosis may come to be controlled by social circumstances over time. The influence of social circumstances on self-report of psychiatric symptoms is generally presumed to be a major cause of low reliability, both inter-rater and repeated measurement, of neo-Kraepelinian diagnoses. Assessment of the contributions of neurophysiological vs. psychosocial factors in a complex clinical presentation is a key challenge in treating schizophrenia spectrum disorders.

The Process-Reactive Continuum

Our modern perspective on the schizophrenia spectrum recognizes that the importance of psychiatric symptoms has been historically overestimated, compared to other dimensions that identify separate groups or subgroups, and also that there are wide individual differences within and across groupings. An important historical example of the nonsymptom dimensions of schizophrenia is the *process-reactive continuum* (Cromwell, 1975), which guided schizophrenia research for decades in the mid-20th century. Originally derived from psychoanalytic hypotheses about subtypes of schizophrenia, the process-reactive distinction came to be understood as a multidimensional continuum, combining developmental measures (e.g., child and adolescent social functioning), genetic information (family history of mental illness), features of the onset (earlier vs. later, sudden vs. gradual), and course of illness features (good vs. poor outcome). At the process end of the continuum are individuals with a family history of the disorder, poor childhood functioning, a gradual onset, predominantly negative symptoms, poor treatment response, poor functioning between episodes, and poor outcome. At the reactive end of the continuum are people with no family history, good functioning up until a sudden onset, predominantly paranoid or affective symptoms, relatively intact functioning between episodes, good treatment response, and good outcome. The people at the two extremes are so different they may appear to represent distinct categories, but the process-reactive dimension is continuous, with many individuals in an intermediate range. Of course, people at different points of the process-reactive continuum tend to have different recovery goals and different treatment and rehabilitation needs.

We are rediscovering the usefulness of the process-reactive continuum as psychopathologists increasingly incorporate evidence from cognitive and behavioral neuroscience. In our contemporary neurodevelopmental understanding of schizophrenia, the process-reactive continuum summarizes the impact of the myriad causal and moderating factors that operate over the course of development to produce dysfunction and disability. For example, the recent development of *overall genetic risk scales* (discussed in Section 2.2) revives the idea in the form of a continuum of risk or severity reflecting the cumulative contributions of multiple genes. The impact on human development of environmental stress and trauma in childhood broadens the range of contributing risk factors beyond genes.

The process-reactive continuum is also relevant to functional distinctions between bipolar disorder and other schizophrenia spectrum disorders. Bipolar disorder is not under the schizophrenia spectrum rubric in DSM-5, but is often considered part of the schizophrenia spectrum in the scientific sense. There is significant overlap in key features, i.e., recurring psychotic episodes, high risk for chronicity and disability, involvement of and impact on families. Treatment approaches also overlap. However, to the degree that a person with a bipolar diagnosis shows characteristics of the reactive end of the process-reactive continuum, especially good premorbid functioning and return to relatively normal functioning between psychotic episodes, the practitioner should consider perspectives and treatment approaches specialized for that subpopulation (e.g., Reiser, Thompson, Johnson, & Suppe, 2017).

There is significant overlap between the symptoms associated with schizophrenia spectrum disorders and those associated with bipolar disorder

Cognitive and Neuropsychological Dimensions

Cognitive dimensions are also important sources of individual differences within the schizophrenia spectrum. In the late 20th century a convergence of two scientific disciplines, experimental psychopathology and neuropsychology, transformed our understanding of schizophrenia. By the 1990s it was credible to propose that schizophrenia is essentially a *neuropsychological disorder*, in the sense that the cognitive impairments measured by neuropsychological instruments play key roles in etiology and the resulting disability. Currently, it is fashionable to characterize schizophrenia as primarily a *cognitive* or *neurocognitive* disorder. Those with the most severe cognitive impairments tend to have the poorest outcomes, and cognitive impairments generally predict functional outcomes better than symptoms.

By the time the DSM-5 was issued in 2013, developmental neuroscience had begun to show how cognitive impairments come about, consolidating our understanding of schizophrenia as a neurodevelopmental disorder with key expressions in the cognitive domain. Today cognitive psychology and neuropsychology paradigms are central to schizophrenia spectrum research. Modern methodology spans the entire cognitive spectrum, from the processes of memory, attention, and perception measured by traditional neuropsychological instruments, to information processing paradigms used in conjunction with advanced brain imaging and electroencephalography, to sophisticated measures of complex social/interpersonal cognition. Some measures can statistically differentiate diagnostic groups within the schizophrenia spectrum (Van Rheenen et al., 2015), but the overlap of distributions is substantial. As new treatment approaches evolve, they increasingly use cognitive measures to individually tailor therapy and to target the cognitive impairments themselves.

Functional Dimensions

For the most practical purposes, the most important dimensions of the schizophrenia spectrum are measures of *personal and social functioning*, including the ability to perform personal care and hygiene, to maintain a home, to get and keep a job or otherwise maintain financial support, to manage personal finances, to make and keep friends, to have intimate relationships, and to have satisfying hobbies and interests. These are the dimensions that determine the type and degree of disability, both of which vary significantly across the schizophrenia spectrum and within people over time. They are the dimensions most important to the people affected. They are frequently targets of treatment, and improvements on these dimensions are frequently personal recovery goals. Severity of functional impairment is weakly correlated with psychiatric symptoms in clinically stable patients.

1.1.4   The Medical Model

As typically used, the phrase *medical model* refers to a combination of presumptions, including: (1) schizophrenia (and other mental illnesses) is a distinct biological disease (i.e., a condition with known etiology, pathophysiology, and course); (2) the symptoms of schizophrenia are the most important targets of treatment; (3) *pharmacotherapy* (drug treatment) is the primary, if not sole treatment for schizophrenia; and (4) psychiatrists, as physicians specializing in medical treatment of mental illnesses, are or should be the primary practitioners, directors, and supervisors of all treatment.

The medical model assumes that pharmacotherapy is always the treatment of choice and that physicians should direct all treatment

The neo-Kraepelinian era arguably represented the epitome of the medical model, but it has been described and criticized in the psychological literature at least since the 1960s, e.g., in the Introduction to Ullman and Krasner's classic 1965 text, *Case Studies in Behavior Modification*. In that context, the medical model should not be too closely associated with biological medicine – it was fully functioning in the psychoanalytic era. The enduring feature of the medical model is not biology, but the primary roles of physicians, the typically subordinate roles of "allied healthcare professions," policies and regulations that support these roles, the ways in which healthcare services are funded and eligible patients identified, and the traditional corporate and management structures of the healthcare industry. Both psychoanalytic and biomedical versions of the medical model have been criticized in the discourse of the recovery movement (further discussed in Section 1.1.6). In recent years investigative journalists and the popular press have joined in criticizing the dubious validity of psychiatric diagnosis, the questionable benefits of psychiatric drugs, and neglect of the psychosocial dimensions of mental illness (e.g., see Robert Whitaker in Further Readings). Modern approaches to treatment and rehabilitation for the schizophrenia spectrum tend to be at best marginally compatible with key features of the medical model, but it persists today as the dominant paradigm in mental health services.

For a period in the 1980s a reductionist medical model was vigorously endorsed by a social movement of parents and family of people diagnosed with schizophrenia. This was in large part a reaction to 1950s-era psychoanalytic theory and practice that identified emotionally aloof parenting as the cause of the disorder. The movement coalesced as the National Alliance for the Mentally Ill (NAMI). To debunk the psychoanalytic theory of the "schizophrenogenic mother," NAMI undertook an extensive public education campaign promoting a neo-Kraepelinian view of schizophrenia as a "brain disease." The "broken brain" imagery of the period (Andreasen, 1984) was particularly appealing for this purpose. Unfortunately, having an incurable disabling brain disease is also quite stigmatizing, and neither public opinion nor mental health policy were positively affected. In the following decades, the competing idea of *recovery from disability* (discussed in the next two sections) overtook reductionism in the advocacy community, and public education now emphasizes the importance of a holistic understanding of mental health and illness. Today renamed National Alliance on Mental Illness, NAMI now includes a broader constituency of people with mental illness and their friends, families, scientists, practitioners, policy scholars, and policy makers.

1.1.5   Psychiatric Rehabilitation

Psychiatric rehabilitation is a holistic approach to treating the schizophrenia spectrum. It is a set of principles concerning the nature of mental illness and disability, an organizational framework for treatment and rehabilitation services, a robust clinical research literature, and an array of specific modalities or treatments for achieving goals and objectives pertinent to recovery. The idea of applying rehabilitation to psychiatric disorders first appeared in the 1940s. Its modern form coalesced later in the 20th century, in the wake of deinstitutionalization and its failures, as a result of a convergence of developments in psychopathology, social learning theory, cognitive and behavioral therapy, public opinion, mental health policy, and a vigorous consumer movement (discussed in the next section). At the center of this convergence was a translation of the psychology of *physical* rehabilitation (i.e., for physical injury) into the modern psychiatric context, by psychologist William Anthony (Anthony, Buell, Sharratt, & Althoff, 1972). The schizophrenia spectrum is a central concern of psychiatric rehabilitation because it represents the most disabling forms of mental illness.

Psychiatric rehabilitation views mental illness as a disability rather than a disease

The key principle of psychiatric rehabilitation is viewing mental illness as a disability to be overcome rather than a disease to be cured (or deemed incurable). This leads to a functional pragmatism that embraces any tool, biological, psychological, or social, that effectively solves problems or achieves goals in the course of recovery. As the schizophrenia spectrum became understood as a disorder of both brain development and psychological development, the importance of addressing multiple levels of human functioning became more obvious, and resonated with psychiatric rehabilitation's multimodal approach. Today psychiatric rehabilitation is considered by its adherents to operate in a *biopsychosocial paradigm*, informed by molecular neuroscience, cognitive neuroscience, systems biology, social learning theory, and the social psychology and sociology of disability. Mercifully, *biosystemic* has become an accepted substitute for naming psychiatric rehabilitation's scientific paradigm, and that term will be used in this discussion hereafter.

Psychiatric rehabilitation is also an inherently interdisciplinary approach, due in large part to its respect for the distributed value of biological, psychological, and sociological methods. Clinical psychologists may play any of several professional roles within a program or service array, from individual or group therapist (using modalities specialized for the schizophrenia spectrum and psychiatric disabilities), to behavior management consultant, to consultant for cognitive and neuropsychological issues, to chief strategist and supervising practitioner of a treatment team managing multiple services and navigating complex sets of problems in pursuit of recovery (Spaulding, Sullivan, & Poland, 2003; Spaulding & Sullivan, 2016a).

Due to its origins in clinical behavioral science, psychiatric rehabilitation is very empirically oriented, emphasizing the need for objective and systematic measurement to assess needs, evaluate treatment effects, and monitor progress toward recovery. This creates challenges in real world implementation, where traditional practitioners and administrators are suspicious or fearful of valid measurement of treatment outcomes. The traditional administrative and professional hierarchies of the medical model are not especially friendly to the methods and procedures of psychiatric rehabilitation, but whether they are absolutely incompatible remains unclear. Working psychiatric rehabilitation programs have been developed in the real world (i.e., outside grant-funded academic research sites), complete with multimodal assessment and treatment, fully integrated with conventional medical regulations and records systems, and their effectiveness in conventional healthcare environments and regulatory regimens has been clearly demonstrated (e.g., Newbill et al., 2011; Paul & Lentz, 1977; Silverstein et al., 2006; Spaulding et al., 2003). However, partly because of conflict with vested interests in the healthcare industry, and partly because of public apathy and persistent stigmatization of mental illness, dissemination of psychiatric rehabilitation has been poor. Today there are important university-based research centers advancing services for the schizophrenia spectrum, and psychiatric rehabilitation in particular, including Boston University, Dartmouth University, the University of Maryland, and UCLA. Several comprehensive textbooks of psychiatric rehabilitation have been published since the turn of the 21st century, representing somewhat different perspectives and emphases, but sharing the key principles (Corrigan, Mueser, Bond, Drake, & Solomon, 2008; Liberman, 2008; Pratt, Gill, Barrett, & Roberts, 2014; Spaulding et al., 2003). Nevertheless, application in the real world falls far short of its potential.

1.1.6   Recovery

The familiar meaning of "recovery" is grounded in our understanding of healing after infectious disease or injury. Recovery begins when the disease is cured or the injurious conditions removed and is complete when the body has repaired its damage and regained full functioning. In application to the schizophrenia spectrum, the idea of recovery has taken on a new meaning (Spaulding, Montague, Avila, & Sullivan, 2016). In psychiatric rehabilitation, recovery means overcoming disabilities and achieving the best possible quality of life. This meaning intersects with the values of the *recovery movement*, a consumerist social movement whose roots arguably extend back to the early 20th century, and which became influential in national mental health policy.

William Anthony, a founding figure in psychiatric rehabilitation, pointed out this intersection in the 1990s. In the recovery movement, the concept acquired connotations of a decent quality of life and hope for a better future, beyond overcoming the effects of mental illness. Although current usage is quite diverse, recovery always includes the ideas of overcoming disability and of treatment and recovery goals being defined with or by the person being treated, typically including normalization of role functioning in addition to remission of symptoms. By implication, recovery connotes a rejection of key features of the medical model.

The recovery movement views schizophrenia spectrum disorder as a disability that can be – and often is – overcome

A heuristically useful distinction among definitions of recovery is between *outcome* and *process*. In recovery as an outcome, a person is recovered when symptoms and disabilities are either no longer present, or are reduced to the point of not interfering significantly with daily living and/or quality of life (i.e., with normal role functions). Defined in this way, recovery can be readily operationalized and measured, facilitating studies of groups of individuals and types of treatment. In contrast, recovery as a process means that the recovering person is rediscovering meaning in life apart from the mental illness and its effects. Recovery in this sense may be independent of treatment or other externally provided services. It is a personal journey for each individual. There is a diversity of opinion in the recovery movement about how much treatment or other services can inform, enhance, or facilitate recovery as a process. Many practitioners, including William Anthony, argue that psychiatric rehabilitation is essentially a toolbox for those pursuing recovery, either as an outcome or a process. Others point out that family and community can provide support for recovery beyond what can be provided by mental health services. Everyone agrees about the importance of the recovering person's active involvement in all services, including selection of outcome criteria and recovery goals.

The ideas of rehabilitation and recovery have had a profound impact on national mental health policy, if not practice. This is evident in a series of federal documents, first a report from the US Surgeon General in 1999, then a report from a special commission appointed by the US President in 2003, then a National Consensus Conference on Mental Health Recovery and Mental Health Systems Transformation in 2004 (U.S. Department of Health and Human Services, 2004). The consensus conference defined recovery from mental illness as "a journey of healing and transformation enabling a person with a mental health problem to live a meaningful life in a community of his or her choice while striving to achieve his or her full potential" (p. 1). Ten "fundamental components" of recovery were enumerated: self-direction, person-centered individualization, empowerment, holistic perspective, expectation of non-linear progress, a strengths-based focus, peer support, respect, personal responsibility of the consumer, and hope for a better future.

The concept of recovery is very different in the context of substance abuse

In the context of the schizophrenia spectrum, "recovery" and "rehabilitation" must not be confused with the same terms used in the addictions/substance abuse context. In the latter, "recovery" derives primarily from the quasi-religious 12-step model historically associated with Alcoholics Anonymous. There are superficial overlaps, e.g., the idea of personal responsibility for change, but recovery in the schizophrenia spectrum is profoundly different from recovery from alcoholism or other addictions. In the substance abuse treatment industry, rehabilitation or "rehab" refers primarily to programs in inpatient or otherwise sequestered settings where the person detoxifies, suffers through withdrawal, and establishes new resolve to abstain or moderate. There is little, if any resemblance to psychiatric rehabilitation programs for people with schizophrenia spectrum disorders.

1.1.7 Evidence-Based Practice

Evidence-based practice is a movement, within the professional and scientific healthcare communities, concerned with the influence of science on clinical practice. It began in the 1990s with broad initiatives by the National Institute of Medicine and became a sustained concern within mental health science, practice, and policy. The concern is that clinical practice in the real world, e.g., selection of specific treatments for specific patients, is insufficiently informed by scientific validation of effectiveness. There is not much debate about that, but there are diverse opinions about what better evidence-based practice should be. A 2006 American Psychological Association Task Force described a relatively circumspect view, that evidence-based practice involves not just consideration of controlled research, but also reliable and data-based professional judgment, and consideration of cultural and other contextual factors that contribute to individual differences and individual needs (recently updated as an APA policy statement; see APA, 2015). This is not necessarily consistent with the view that clinical practice should strictly adhere to the findings and implications of controlled experiments. Debate about exactly what evidence-based practice in clinical psychology should look like continues today.

Of course, the debate about how much and how literally science should inform clinical practice is about as old as clinical psychology itself. For the purposes of this book, the aspects of evidence-based practice most relevant to the schizophrenia spectrum are: (1) scientific psychopathology research provides important insights into the nature of schizophrenia spectrum disorders, including insights that guide development of beneficial treatments and other services; (2) controlled treatment trials provide useful information about what approaches work best for what problems, although they must still be validated in the real world; (3) evidence-based practice also requires *practice-based evidence*, that is, clinical practice should be structured as much as possible to generate reliable information on treatment effects, on an individual, case-wise basis, to validate progress and expected benefits (Spaulding & Deogun, 2011).

Evidence-based practice requires practice-based evidence

Psychiatric rehabilitation is especially amenable to this view of evidence-based practice, due to its origins in the psychology of rehabilitation and its emphasis on operational identification of recovery goals and objectives, its accumulation of specific, experimentally validated modalities and techniques, its use of quantitative data generated by treatment to evaluate progress toward goals and objectives on an individual basis, and its attention to the personal values and desires of the recovering person.

1.2   Definition

The limited construct validity of "schizophrenia" makes any particular definition somewhat arbitrary, but even arbitrary definitions may have some utility. The principle value of defining schizophrenia and schizophrenia spectrum is arguably in the domain of scientific research. However its main function in research is not as an *independent variable*, i.e., denoting a distinct group to be compared with other groups, but as an *inclusion variable*, i.e., denoting an indistinct group wherein features of interest are expected to be conveniently frequent or accessible. Research does not usually include groups that "almost but not quite meet the diagnostic criteria for schizophrenia," and there is little reason to expect that such a group would be different from one that does. There is no longer a presumption that any feature of schizophrenia is unique to schizophrenia, and there are many different combinations of symptoms and other features that meet the diagnostic criteria for schizophrenia. Most modern research seeks to understand specific abnormalities often found in groups diagnosed with "schizophrenia," and that understanding usually generalizes to the same abnormalities when found in other groups. With all that qualification in mind, since the DSM-III appeared, research studies have almost universally used DSM criteria, or those of its international counterpart, the *International Classification of Disease* (*ICD*), to define "schizophrenia." With the appearance of "schizophrenia spectrum" in DSM-5, diagnostic criteria can now also be used to define that multi-diagnosis grouping.

With the exception of elimination of the subtypes (paranoid, etc.), the diagnostic criteria have changed minimally between DSM-III and DSM-5. The key criterion for all diagnoses in the family of "Schizophrenia Spectrum and Other Psychotic Disorders" is abnormality in at least one of five domains: hallucinations, delusions, disorganized thinking and speech, abnormal motor behavior (including catatonia), and negative symptoms. The schizophrenia spectrum disorders are distinguished from the others when other conditions that may cause psychosis are ruled out, e.g., medical illnesses or intoxication.

The diagnosis of *schizophrenia* requires symptoms in at least two of the psychotic domains; a significant decrement in personal and social functioning associated with symptom onset, or failure to achieve expected levels if onset is early; continuous signs of disorder for at least six months; no affective symptoms (depression, mania) or affective symptoms that are present for a minority of the time; and symptoms that are not attributable to a medical condition or substance abuse. If the criteria are met, the diagnosis is further specified as being in its first episode or having a history of multiple episodes, and the clinician notes whether the episode is ongoing ("acute") or in partial or full remission (i.e., the symptoms are reduced in severity or absent).

> **The diagnosis of schizophrenia requires continuous signs of the disorder for at least six months**

The other disorders in the schizophrenia spectrum represent variations in symptom picture or time course. *Brief psychotic disorder* applies when all symptom criteria are met for at least one day but less than one month. *Schizophreniform disorder* applies when all symptom criteria for schizophrenia are met, and duration since onset has been more than one month but less than six. For *delusional disorder* and *catatonia*, those symptoms are present but the presentation does not otherwise meet all symptom criteria for schizophrenia. For *schizo-affective disorder*, the presentation includes significant depression or mania along with the other psychotic symptoms. There are various other specifiers that may apply to the various diagnoses. Each DSM-5 diagnosis is indexed to a corresponding diagnosis in ICD-9 and ICD-10.

1.3   Epidemiology

The World Health Organization monitors the prevalence of schizophrenia worldwide (Hopper, Harrison, Janca, & Sartorius, 2007). Estimates of the prevalence of schizophrenia in the general population range from about .5 to 1.5%. That is, about .5–1.5% of all people meet the DSM or ICD diagnostic criteria for schizophrenia at some point in their lives. The variability in estimates is due at least in part to variability in diagnostic criteria. The .5% figure is probably closest to incidence of schizophrenia as strictly defined by DSM criteria. The 1.5% is probably closest to the proportion of people disabled by disorders in the schizophrenia spectrum. The diagnosis is most commonly made in late adolescence or early adulthood. Cross-cultural studies suggest the rate is fairly consistent across cultures. However, there may be differences in *morbidity*, the degree to which the illness causes disability or other impairments. People in more industrial cultures who meet diagnostic criteria for schizophrenia suffer more severe disabilities than those in less industrial cultures, and outcome is generally poorer in the developed world.

> **The worldwide lifetime prevalence of schizophrenia is .5–1.5%**

Epidemiological findings have been influential in the evolution of the view that schizophrenia is among other things a neurodevelopmental disorder. Patterns of relationships between the incidence of schizophrenia and factors such as birth complications, *neurological soft signs* (abnormalities that do not denote specific neurological disease, e.g., mixed lateral dominance), minor physical anomalies (e.g., malformation of capillaries in the fingernail bed), season of birth (e.g., the second trimester of gestation occurs during a cold season, increasing the risk of viral infection), and environmental stressors during gestation or infancy (droughts, famines, war, child abuse), all suggest that developmental compromise of the central nervous system (CNS) is often an etiological factor. The stable cross-cultural incidence rate is also cited as evidence of a common underlying biological etiology. However, the variable morbidity across cultures indicates the importance of environmental factors as well.

Socioeconomic status has historically been associated with the epidemiology of the schizophrenia spectrum, but its causal role has remained ambiguous. There is no question that people with schizophrenia spectrum disorders are impoverished and inhabit the lower end of measures of social class, but that occurs almost by definition. These are disabling disorders, and even in cultures where disabled people are protected from abject deprivation, they do not fare as well as the general population. The issue is therefore one of causation vs. selection. It has proven difficult to establish a causal connection between socioeconomic factors and the incidence or course of schizophrenia, although there appear to be myriad interactions between risk for schizophrenia spectrum disorder and poverty, cultural context, local community factors, and individual characteristics, including gender (e.g., Berg et al., 2015)

1.4   Course and Prognosis

Kraepelin's presumption of lifelong deterioration has been disproved by nearly a century of research. Bleuler proposed a "law of thirds" of schizophrenia outcome: one third of all affected people suffer severe lifelong disability, one third recover substantially, and one third experience a mixed course with some persistent disability but also significant recovery. Bleuler's law of thirds remains roughly supported, but the implicit belief that there is no recovery from schizophrenia has persisted, and is held today by many mental health professionals. However, rigorous large-scale research studies have shown that recovery can be virtually complete in many individuals (e.g., Harding, Brooks, Ashikaga, Strauss, & Breier, 1987; Jobe & Harrow, 2005), especially where there are appropriate community-based mental health services. Even those in Bleuler's most unfortunate third can achieve significant improvements in their personal and social functioning and quality of life if provided modern treatment and rehabilitation. Persistent disbelief in recovery from schizophrenia by professionals who should know better may be indistinguishable from the broader prejudice, discrimination, and stigmatization that people with severe mental illness have suffered for centuries.

Outcome in the schizophrenia spectrum is complex and multidimensional. For the purposes of this discussion, it is heuristically convenient to separately consider short-term and long-term outcome.

1.4.1   Short-Term Outcomes

The shortest-term expected outcome in treatment of the schizophrenia spectrum is reduction of psychotic symptoms, including affective symptoms of psychotic-level severity. The treatment most closely associated with psychotic symptom reduction is antipsychotic medication. Pharmacological treatment has been intensively researched for half a century, yet controversies continue. Antipsychotic medications exert their primary effects in days to weeks (although the trajectory may extend for months), but it remains unclear how much reduction of psychotic symptoms leads to positive longer-term outcomes. The medical model's preoccupation with symptom reduction, to the neglect of more meaningful recovery goals, is a principle complaint of the recovery movement. Overall, estimates of the proportion of people that gain any measurable benefit from antipsychotics gravitate to about 75%. That means about 25% gain no benefit, and very few if any recover their full premorbid functioning with medication alone. This estimate is based on short-term effects (often in terms of weeks) and often on criteria as weak as a 20% reduction in positive symptoms. In real world contexts, where co-occurring substance abuse and treatment nonadherence are common, rates of meaningful benefit are often lower.

The medical model focuses on symptom reduction rather than recovery

One in four people treated with antipsychotics will receive little or no benefit from treatment

Specialized forms of cognitive behavioral therapy also produce relief from symptoms, including symptoms that have been refractory to medication, in a relatively short-term time frame. The treatment effect appears to involve reducing the distress and disruption of the symptoms, at least as much as reducing the symptoms per se.

Relapse, i.e., having another psychotic episode after initial improvement, is another much-studied short-term outcome of antipsychotic medication. Of course, medication is useless when not ingested, and nonadherence is a known cause of relapse. However, when adherence is ensured, e.g., with injectable long-acting formulations, the relapse rate may still be as high as 50% per year. Relapse rates may be just as sensitive to factors other than medication adherence, including illicit drug or alcohol use and the emotional tone of the family. Evidence for the latter is that psychosocial treatments, e.g., social skills training and family therapy, can reduce or postpone relapse (see Section 4.1). Also, the effectiveness of medication in controlling symptoms or preventing relapse appears to dissipate a few years after onset (Harrow et al., 2014).

Social skills training can reduce or postpone relapse

Symptom remission and relapse are key outcome measures in studies of *first episode treatment*, i.e., specialized programs to identify and treat schizophrenia spectrum disorders within months of onset. First episode treatment has seen a dramatic increase in researchers' attention over the past decade, due to the possibility that good short-term outcome, e.g., prevention of relapse in the first year after onset, reduces chronicity and improves long-term outcome. Longitudinal studies indicate that a delay between onset and treatment produces poorer outcome, and the impact of delay in psychosocial services may be even greater than that for medication. Full symptom remission within one year is achieved by a large majority of patients in specialized early intervention programs, although relapse rates can approach 100% over 1-2 years for patients who engage in substance abuse or abruptly stop their medication. Vocational outcomes are also improved. In 2012 the National Institute of Mental Health launched a national multi-site controlled trial of first episode treatment, and early analyses indicate the expected short-term outcomes were achieved (Kane et al., 2016). It remains to be seen whether such remarkably positive results will lead to enhanced recovery in the longer term.

The efficacy of antipsychotic medication for stabilizing the psychotic episode is beyond dispute. However, alternative nonpharmacological approaches to acute psychosis have also produced good results. Psychiatrist Loren Mosher and his colleagues (e.g., Mosher & Bola, 2000) have demonstrated that, in many cases, young patients undergoing their first or second psychotic episode can be successfully treated without medication in a community-residential setting with specially trained direct care staff. Strauss and Carpenter (1977) also reported successful treatment of acute schizophrenia without drugs. Both approaches incur risks and benefits. More research is needed to determine who benefits most from which approach, especially considering that pharmacotherapy is ineffective for a significant proportion of people. Also, the timing of the administration of medication (early or later in the course of illness) may moderate the effects of pharmacological treatment of acute psychosis and needs to be investigated further (discussed in Section 1.4). Ultimately, it may prove feasible to offer people a choice of drug or nondrug treatment during psychotic episodes.

Young patients undergoing their first or second psychotic episode often can be successfully treated without medication

1.4.2   Long-Term Outcomes

The role of antipsychotic medication in the longer term is increasingly controversial. In the formative years of psychiatric rehabilitation, Paul and Lentz (1977) observed that an unexpectedly high proportion of "treatment refractory" patients who made substantial gains in their social learning treatment program were successfully discharged and had a stable community tenure after medication had been discontinued. More recently, rigorous longitudinal research indicates that long-term medication is unnecessary for a substantial proportion of people with schizophrenia spectrum disorders (Harrow, Jobe, & Faull, 2014). Similar conclusions are supported by the outcomes of first episode treatment programs (Wunderink, Nieboer, Wiersma, Sytema, & Nienhuis, 2013). Although discontinuation or reduction increases risk of relapse for 3 years after onset, after 7 years there is no difference in relapse rates, and patients who achieved initial stabilization and then underwent dose reduction or discontinuation had a 40% better rate of functional recovery than patients with similar early outcomes who stayed on their original stabilization dose of medication (Wunderink et al., 2013). Thus the shorter-term benefits may be superseded by longer-term benefits.

Psychiatric rehabilitation and the recovery movement have created a new longer-term expectation for psychopharmacology (and any other treatment), beyond symptom suppression, to facilitate recovery of personal and social functioning. It was recognized early in antipsychotic drug research that whatever they may do for symptoms, antipsychotics do not get the patient a job, or friends, or a place to live. There is no evidence that sustained symptom suppression or any other long-term benefit of antipsychotics contributes to achieving these key recovery goals. Bellack, Schooler et al. (2004) found no medication effects on social competence or problem solving.

Another disappointment has been the failure of pharmacotherapy to address cognitive and neurocognitive impairments, increasingly seen as critical moderators of long-term outcome. The NIMH MATRICS project (discussed in Section 3.1.2) was conceived in large part to facilitate discovery of drugs for that purpose. Some antipsychotics may have marginally significant benefits in the neurocognitive or cognitive domains, but these are overwhelmed and eclipsed by the much larger effects of comprehensive psychiatric rehabilitation (Liberman, Gutkind, et al., 2002). There are also detrimental effects on cognition from sedating side effects of antipsychotic medications, and the anticholinergic effects associated with many of these drugs have been shown to impair memory in people with schizophrenia. Medications have not been shown to be effective for cognitive impairments for people with schizophrenia (Barch, 2010), and documentation of medication effects on negative symptoms remains elusive.

> **Antipsychotic medications often impair memory and have little effect on negative symptoms**

The complicated short-term and long-term outcome findings demand circumspection in clinical practice. The medical risks of antipsychotic medication, e.g., neurological side effects, obesity, and diabetes mellitus, are significant. Nonadherence to prescribed antipsychotic medication can reach up to 75%, and may not be simply neglectful or irrational. Many patients discontinue medication because of insufficient efficacy (Kahn et al., 2008), and prescription of unnecessary medications or excessive dosages is common

(Robinson et al., 2015). Introduction of the so-called atypical antipsychotics in the 1990s reduced neurological side effects but increased metabolic side effects, and did not improve the older drugs' effectiveness in treating psychotic symptoms. There is hope in the psychopharmacology research community that genomics will enable more strategic use of medication, including antipsychotics, but this is not expected to become clinically feasible in the near future. Despite voluminous knowledge about drug actions in research studies, the actual decision-making behind psychopharmacotherapy remains largely unknown. Attempts to formulate prescriptive practice in decision algorithms, arguably comparable to formulating psychotherapy in procedural manuals, have produced disappointing results, and it appears unlikely that there will be any major breakthroughs or new approaches in psychopharmacotherapy for schizophrenia spectrum disorders in the foreseeable future. Several large pharmaceutical firms have curtailed research and development in the serious mental illness market. Under those conditions, the most pressing research issue is to better understand how to optimize use of our existing pharmacopeia in individual patients, targeting specific problems while pursuing an array of individualized rehabilitation and recovery goals.

Paul and Lentz (1977) demonstrated that even "treatment-refractory" patients could benefit from treatment when treatment consisted of an intensive social learning-based inpatient program followed by gradually reducing aftercare. In that study, long-stay institutional patients who were treated in the social learning program achieved a 97% discharge rate (compared to a 50% rate in traditional, custodial care), 1200% improvement in adaptive, social, cognitive, and instrumental outcomes (compared to negligible improvements with other treatment models), with only 11% needing antipsychotic medication at discharge, compared to 100% of patients in the custodial care condition.

Paul and Lentz conducted a classic study demonstrating the efficacy of a social learning program in an inpatient setting

Even without intensive treatment and rehabilitation, many studies have revealed longer-term outcomes that are better than expected. About 20–25% of the patients in these studies regain normal levels of personal and social functioning, with an additional 25–30% significantly improved, and some two thirds without psychotic symptoms.

One set of long-term studies in New England provided an opportunity to assess the role of mental health and social services in outcome (DeSisto, Harding, McCormick, Ashikaga, & Brooks, 1995; Harding et al. 1987). In the 1950s Vermont had developed comprehensive community-based rehabilitation programming that was linked to state hospital census reduction. Maine had not, relying instead on medication and conventional hospital-based aftercare services. During the follow-up period, Vermont subjects worked more, had fewer symptoms, and had better community adjustment and global functioning than Maine subjects. Subsequent analyses (Mojtabai, Nicholson, Isohanni, Jones, & Partennen, 1998) have corroborated the role of psychosocial services in long-term outcome.

Recovery as a Long-Term Outcome

Higher expectations inspired by the recovery movement, and more rigorous quantitative measurement of recovery as an outcome, led to sobering reconsideration of older outcome data. A meta-analysis of 50 studies of long-term outcome (Jääskeläinen et al., 2013) found that the proportion of people who

Research has documented recovery rates of 11–53% for schizophrenia spectrum disorders

met holistic criteria for recovery ranged from 53% down to 11%. Much, if not most of the variability is attributable to methodological differences, especially operational definitions of recovery. By the stringent criteria of the meta-analysis, the median proportion that showed sustained recovery in either clinical or social domains was only 13.5%. In the time frame studied, that translates to about 1% of the subject population achieving recovery per year. The meta-analysis generated no evidence of improvement in rates of recovery over time. There was no evidence of different prognosis for males and females, inconsistent with historical findings (using different outcome criteria) and predominant beliefs in the research community. Interestingly, the results are not affected by whether neo-Kraepelinian diagnostic criteria are rigorously applied. This further corroborates the value of the schizophrenia spectrum concept.

Much of the research on longer-term outcome has been conducted in the context of experimental studies of specific treatment modalities, psychosocial as well as pharmacological. This will be described for the respective modalities in Section 4.1 on treatment.

1.5   Differential Diagnosis

Because there is no single feature that is common to all cases of schizophrenia and no test that can confirm the diagnosis, diagnosis is essentially a process of elimination. When the clinical presentation meets criteria for schizophrenia or another schizophrenia spectrum disorder as defined by DSM-5 or ICD-10, and other medical conditions (including intoxication) are ruled out, the generally accepted diagnostic criteria are met.

After six months, the diagnosis of schizophreniform disorder changes to schizophrenia

A patient presenting with an initial psychotic episode can be very difficult to diagnose, due to the duration criterion that differentiates schizophrenia from some other psychotic disorders. A patient with the requisite symptoms should be given a diagnosis of schizophreniform disorder if the duration of the condition appears to be shorter than 6 months. After 6 months, the diagnosis changes to schizophrenia. It is also often not possible to differentiate between schizophrenia and bipolar disorder with psychotic features during the initial psychotic episode. This is because both can present with the same psychotic symptoms, and, as discussed in the next section, agitation and mood symptoms are common during acute psychotic episodes. In such cases, information about response to treatment and subsequent clinical course determine the diagnosis.

1.6   Co-Occurring Conditions

People diagnosed with schizophrenia spectrum disorders often have additional psychiatric and medical problems not subsumed by the diagnosis. This section describes the psychiatric and non-psychiatric conditions that frequently co-occur with schizophrenia spectrum disorders. The term *co-occurring* is practically synonymous with the older medical term *comorbidity*, but the former is generally preferred today because of problematic and unnecessary implications of "morbid." Similarly, the term co-occurring *disorders* may imply that all co-occurring conditions are separately diagnosed disorders, but many are not.

1.6.1   Psychiatric Conditions

Depression and Suicide

Depression commonly co-occurs with schizophrenia, especially among patients who are aware that what is happening to them represents a mental illness or disorder. Lifetime estimates of major depression in people diagnosed with schizophrenia typically range from 25–33% of patients, with some studies reporting rates as high as 80%. Estimates of the rate of schizophrenia patients who meet criteria for a depressive syndrome at a single point in time have been reported to be as high as 10% among inpatients and 50% among outpatients.

Suicide is a major problem in schizophrenia. Estimates of the lifetime frequency of suicide attempts among people with the disorder range from 20–50%, and multiple studies have reported that close to 10% of people diagnosed with schizophrenia kill themselves. While suicide in schizophrenia may have multiple causes, including command hallucinations, depression is generally identified as the major precipitating factor.

Approximately 10% of people diagnosed with schizophrenia will commit suicide

Substance Abuse (SA)

As a group people diagnosed with schizophrenia abuse alcohol and street drugs more than the general population, with estimates as high as 50%. Estimates of cigarette smoking have been as high as 90%. Various theories have been proposed to account for this high rate of tobacco use, including the idea that smoking reduces side effects by lowering blood levels of antipsychotic medication, and that it improves cognitive functioning by stimulating the nicotinic form of cholinergic receptor, which can be abnormal in the schizophrenia spectrum. In addition, the addictive potential of tobacco may be higher in people with schizophrenia spectrum disorders than in other populations. Use of alcohol and street drugs in people diagnosed with schizophrenia is often a critical treatment target because it can increase psychotic symptoms, leading to relapse and re-hospitalization.

In the past decade the role of substance abuse in the schizophrenia spectrum has been somewhat obfuscated by policy language in government and the mental health industry that emphasizes the "comorbidity" of substance abuse and psychiatric disorders. Substance abuse is certainly high in the schizophrenia spectrum, but in mental health policy comorbidity refers primarily to anxiety, depression, and personality disorder. This usage began as part of the long-term evolution of public opinion and healthcare policy about alcoholism. Unlike schizophrenia spectrum disorders, alcoholism underwent a substantial change in stigmatization in the mid-20th century, being seen increasingly as a type of illness, not a moral failing. However, actual funding of treatment lagged behind public acceptance, in part because the alcoholism treatment industry had remained fairly separate from the healthcare and mental health industries. With a closer association between alcoholism and recognized psychiatric diagnoses, canonized by the medical term "comorbidity," funding for joint treatment became more politically acceptable, and this acceptance generalized to other addictions, creating a new economics in the substance abuse treatment industry. Unfortunately, the funding for this generalization was usually not new, but rather was shifted away from other mental health resources, especially resources associated with the historical psychiatric institutional population. The effects of such shifting can include dismantling of specialized services developed for people with schizophrenia spectrum disorders (Spaulding & Sullivan, 2016a).

SA comorbid with anxiety, depression, and personality disorder is different from SA occurring in schizophrenia spectrum disorders. In the former, the chief source of disability is the SA, not the co-occurring disorder. In the latter, the disability stems primarily from psychosis and cognitive impairment, not SA. Standard treatment of SA and co-occurring anxiety, depression, or personality disorder usually consists of separate treatment of the SA, most often with variants of the 12-step model associated with Alcoholics Anonymous, and treatment of the other disorder with medication and/or psychotherapy as they would be used in patients without SA. Modalities thought to be effective with SA in general are not so in people with schizophrenia spectrum disorders. Treatment of SA problems in that population requires specialized approaches for the SA, integrated and coordinated with the broader array of modalities in a recovery-oriented psychiatric rehabilitation program (Mueser & Gingerich, 2013).

Repetitive Behaviors

Polydipsia is common among hospitalized patients with schizophrenia

Polydipsia, excessive water intake, is frequent among hospitalized patients, with rates reported as high as 25%. This is a dangerous condition because it can cause electrolyte imbalances ("water intoxication"), leading to delirium, cardiac arrhythmias, and even death. Other repetitive behaviors that may be found among severely ill patients include pica, bulimia, and hoarding.

Obsessive-Compulsive Symptoms

Obsessive-compulsive symptoms are found among schizophrenia patients more frequently than in the general population, often meeting diagnostic criteria for OCD. The presence of obsessive-compulsive symptomatology in schizophrenia is thought to be a poor prognostic indicator. Comorbidity of schizophrenia with obsessive-compulsive symptoms may reflect a common corticostriatal brain system dysregulation, possibly linked to common genetic vulnerabilities.

Anxiety Symptoms and Disorders

Recent studies suggest that anxiety is a significant clinical problem in many patients diagnosed with schizophrenia, both during the initial psychotic episode and over the long term. Anxiety problems can occur as generalized anxiety or as discrete panic attacks. In some cases anxiety may appear to be clinically independent of psychotic symptoms, whereas in other cases it may appear to be a result of hearing command hallucinations or of past experiences of psychosis, i.e., a form of PTSD caused by experiencing psychotic symptoms.

Intellectual Disability

Intellectual disability (previously known as *mental retardation*), like the schizophrenia spectrum, is a subgroup of disorders, some with known etiologies, having in common a generalized compromise of cognitive development with consequent impairment of personal and social functioning. In the DSM-5 it is in the family of neurodevelopmental disorders. The prevalence of schizophrenia spectrum disorders in people with intellectual disabilities is up to four times higher than in the general population. Co-occurrence is as high as 50%. There are multiple plausible etiological mechanisms common to intellectual disability and the schizophrenia spectrum, and they probably interact to a considerable degree (Waltereit, Banaschewski, Meyer-Lindenberg, & Poustka, 2014). Differential diagnosis is complicated due to limitations associated with intellectually disabled individuals' abilities to communicate symptoms. Additionally, parsing out disorganized thinking and behavior attributable to the intellectual disability vs. a psychotic disorder can be challenging, especially for individuals with moderate to severe intellectual disabilities, and more research on schizophrenia spectrum disorders in people with intellectual disabilities is needed. There are important treatment implications when the two disorders co-occur. For example, psychotherapies and psychiatric rehabilitation interventions may need to be modified to accommodate individuals' intellectual limitations.

> **Schizophrenia spectrum disorders frequently co-occur with intellectual disabilities**

Autism

In DSM-5 autism is defined as a spectrum, but unlike the schizophrenia spectrum, *autism spectrum disorder* (ASD) is a single specific diagnosis. Many of the cognitive and behavioral impairments observed in autism appear similar to ones observed in the schizophrenia spectrum, especially those associated with language and social information processing. The two diagnoses co-occur at statistically elevated levels and share genetic and neurophysiological features. As with intellectual disability, multiple etiological factors probably interact to produce a range of consequences. Since both diagnoses subsume heterogeneous groups of individuals, it is difficult to conclude that any feature other than the adolescent/adult onset of schizophrenia distinguishes between them. During periods between acute psychotic episodes, autistic features may generate more functional disability than residual schizophrenia spectrum features.

Learning and Language Disorders

The lifetime prevalence of schizophrenia in people with learning disorders is significantly higher than in the general population, with estimates up to 12%. It is unclear whether this is because learning disabilities are separate vulnerability factors for schizophrenia, or whether some neurodevelopmental abnormalities in the schizophrenia spectrum also produce impairments similar to learning disorders. The brains of people with both disorders structurally resemble those of people diagnosed with schizophrenia alone more than those with learning disorder alone. *Dyslexia* (a specific learning disorder) is associated with abnormalities in integration of complex visual information (e.g., determining an object's shape and its motion), also observed in schizophrenia. Patients diagnosed with both disorders, compared to patients with only schizophrenia, have higher rates of negative symptoms, episodic memory deficits, soft neurological signs, and epilepsy, and require higher levels of care. It may prove useful to identify a subgroup within the schizophrenia spectrum whose neurodevelopmental abnormalities include language-related ones. In the coming decade, the developmental neuroscience of language and learning disorders will provide important new understandings of the schizophrenia spectrum and other neurodevelopmental disorders.

Attention Deficit Hyperactivity Disorder

Childhood ADHD increases the risk for adult schizophrenia spectrum disorders

Attention deficit hyperactivity disorder (ADHD) is another neurodevelopmental disorder whose presence elevates risk for an adult schizophrenia spectrum disorder, presumably because of genetic and developmental vulnerabilities found in both disorders. Even if children with ADHD do not develop a schizophrenia spectrum disorder in adulthood, about 90% continue to experience cognitive impairment of variable severity as adults. The cognitive impairments tend to be in the *executive* neuropsychological domain, where many of the impairments of schizophrenia spectrum disorders are also found. As a result, it can be impossible to determine whether such impairment is a continuation of the childhood disorder, or an aspect of the adult-onset disorder. It is unknown whether optimal treatment would be different, but standard pharmacological treatment of adult attention deficits is different from treatment of psychosis. Either way, the idea of a persistent neurocognitive impairment in an adult with a schizophrenia spectrum disorder reminds us that the disorder is not simply the episodic occurrence of psychosis. Whether of childhood or adult onset, residual executive impairment contributes heavily to functional disability.

Violent Behavior

A controversial topic related to schizophrenia (and to mental illness in general) is whether psychotic disorders increase risk for violence. The general belief in society (including in Hollywood and the popular media) is that people with psychotic disorders are more violent than other people. This contrasts sharply with the message that schizophrenia does not increase the risk for violence, delivered by advocates and consumers, but the belief that violence is linked with schizophrenia spectrum disorders clearly contributes to stigma and bad treatment. Both these positions are too extreme (Silverstein et al., 2015). The reality is complex:

The relationship between psychotic disorders and risk for violence is complex

- People with schizophrenia spectrum disorders are more likely to be victims than perpetrators of violence, but victimization often follows a violent act by the victim.
- The presence of a psychotic disorder does increase the risk for violent behavior, but only by a few percentage points above other risk factors, such as being young, male, unemployed, and using street drugs.
- Most acts of violence committed by people with schizophrenia occur in the context of untreated psychosis, with many occurring at first episode prior to treatment.
- About 40% of people with schizophrenia who commit violent acts are high in *trait psychopathy*. In this group, violent behavior is typically carefully planned and is independent of level of psychotic symptoms. While reduction of psychotic symptoms reduces violence significantly in violent patients without psychopathy, it does not affect violence in patients high in psychopathy.

Although the risk of violence attributed to schizophrenia is small but significant after controlling for all other factors, there are many patients who are at high risk for violent behavior, due to the presence of multiple risk factors. These risks must be carefully identified and managed. Unfortunately, even when risk for violence is identified (which is rarely done in treatment settings), treatment plans rarely reflect this fact.

1.6.2   Medical Conditions

People with schizophrenia spectrum disorders have a life expectancy more than 20 years shorter than the general population. This is not primarily due to psychiatric causes, by e.g., suicide, but results from the same causes that shorten life in the general population. It is thought to be due to multiple factors including living in poorer neighborhoods, reduced access to health care, reduced initiative in seeking healthcare, poorer nutrition, and effects of tobacco, alcohol, and drug abuse, and other unhealthy habits. One condition specifically related to smoking that has been found to be elevated in schizophrenia is chronic obstructive pulmonary disease (COPD). A second condition that appears to be related to impaired decision making, including that secondary to drug use, is an increased prevalence of HIV infection.

Schizophrenia spectrum disorders decrease life expectancy by 20 years

Several medical conditions may result from taking psychiatric medications. In DSM-5, *Medication-induced Movement Disorders and Other Adverse Effects of Medication* has been elevated to a major diagnostic family. Medications used to treat schizophrenia spectrum disorders account for a disproportionate share of these problems. Many patients experience significant weight gain when taking atypical antipsychotics (e.g., an average gain of 30 lbs. when taking olanzapine; see Section 4.1.2). This obesity can then cause other medical problems, such as sleep apnea, cardiovascular problems, and diabetes. While some cases of diabetes may be a direct result of the medication itself, it is generally accepted that many cases are secondary to weight gain. Either way, obesity and diabetes are recognized as serious complications of antipsychotic drug treatment, needing systematic management in the course of treating the psychotic disorder (Stahl, 2013, pp. 173-180). Interestingly, however, some of the risk for medical conditions such as metabolic syndrome, diabetes, and hypertension may be related to the genetic vulnerability to schizophrenia, as these conditions are already elevated early in the course, even at first episode. Even so, there is likely to be an interaction between genetic vulnerability, medication use, and a history of unhealthy lifestyles that exacerbates these problems, especially with increasing illness chronicity.

Weight gain is a common side effect for patients taking atypical antipsychotics

Medical complications that can result from first-generation antipsychotic medications include *tardive dyskinesia* (involuntary muscle activity, often involving the tongue or face), dystonic reactions, muscle rigidity, and *akithesia*, a subjective sense of restlessness, often associated with pacing. In the 1970s and 1980s, the strategy of initiating medication with high doses (i.e., "rapid neuroleptization") led to many cases of *neuroleptic malignant syndrome* (NMS), a life-threatening condition. NMS is characterized by fever, muscular rigidity, altered mental status, and autonomic dysfunction.

Side effects associated with first-generation antipsychotic medications include tardive dyskinesia, akithesia, and neuroleptic malignant syndrome

1.7   Diagnostic and Other Assessment Procedures

Upon first clinical detection of psychotic symptoms, the first priority is to assess the patient's safety, including risk to self or others. Regardless of the diagnosis, or whether or not an "acute episode" has been deemed "stabilized," the symptoms and other impairments may occur at virtually any level of severity. The identified patient may insist that everything is fine, or may express a delusional grasp of the situation. The urgent task is to determine to what degree the patient is in imminent danger and, if so, what legal as well as clinical responses are necessary. This is not simply a diagnostic assessment. Even if symptoms and impairments are severe, risk is moderated if the patient is amenable to treatment and other services, if there is supportive family, and if the patient has a place to live and is connected to social support services.

If the patient is not accepting treatment or other help, un-moderated risks may necessitate legal interventions, e.g., competency determinations, guardianship actions, or civil commitment. Such interventions require formal assessments by qualified mental health professionals, especially competence and risk assessments, and the psychologist is often the professional best positioned and prepared to provide them. Liaison with attorneys, courts, mental health boards, and other entities of the legal system is often a crucial activity at this stage of the assessment process.

The second priority, which often must be pursued in tandem with the first, is to rule out acute and possibly lethal medical conditions that may cause psychosis. Psychotic symptoms are usually observed first by family members, friends, teachers, family healthcare providers, law enforcement officers, or emergency personnel, and sometimes by the person with the symptoms. Presence of the symptoms is usually confirmed by a healthcare professional, based on information from people in the identified patient's social milieu and mental status examination. Involvement of healthcare professionals may be substantially delayed, especially if the identified patient denies or is unaware of a psychiatric problem. Often, a year or more elapses between the first appearance of psychotic symptoms and evaluation by a qualified practitioner. When the first practitioner to observe psychosis is a clinical psychologist, the expected response would normally be to refer the patient for a preliminary medical evaluation to rule out acute medical causes of psychosis, whether or not the psychologist expects to have continuing involvement in the case.

The diagnosis of schizophrenia spectrum disorder is made by ruling out other explanations for aberrant behavior

The schizophrenia spectrum diagnosis is made as other medical conditions are ruled out. The specific diagnosis within the schizophrenia spectrum should usually be supported by a structured interview specifically designed for that purpose. If there is no previous history of psychosis, an initial diagnosis of schizophreniform disorder may have to be updated 6 months after onset.

As soon as possible, an interdisciplinary treatment team must be assembled, to include the patient, a legally appointed substitute decision maker (i.e., a guardian) when applicable, key family members, and all providers expected to have a role in assessment, treatment, and rehabilitation. The overall context set by the patient's legal status has a profound effect on when and how this happens. In some circumstances, it is possible to assemble a treatment team even if the identified patient declines to participate, in others, not. The psychologist may have to operate "solo," as a consultant to the family or others, for some time before a functional treatment team can be assembled.

When the treatment team is assembled the next step is to formulate a comprehensive treatment and rehabilitation plan, based as much as possible on the identified patient's rehabilitation and recovery goals. The plan must identify all the problems that are barriers to better functioning and recovery, as identified by evidence-based assessments that address biological, psychological, behavioral, and social levels of functioning. The plan must usually anticipate a series of stages, wherein reaching one set of goals is necessary before the next stage can begin. Sometimes the goals of the first stage are focused on simply engaging the patient in the treatment team process.

A psychiatric rehabilitation and recovery plan is structured to allow separate, quantitative assessment of identified problems and progress toward goals (this will be discussed in detail in Chapter 3). Treatment and rehabilitation proceed as a series of quasi-experimental trials, wherein choice of specific modalities reflects the treatment team's collective hypothesis about the cause of each problem and its optimal solution. When expectations for outcome are not supported by the data, the team must re-enter the process, and consider new hypotheses and alternative treatments, until the goals are met.

2

Theories and Models of the Schizophrenia Spectrum

Modern etiological theories of the schizophrenia spectrum have two key features: (1) they make extensive use of the concept of vulnerability or diathesis-stress, and (2) they reflect a biosystemic paradigm in which biological, psychological, and social processes interact reciprocally. The second feature is the more recent development in the march of science. Many of the older theories have a reductionist connotation, i.e., they imply that "schizophrenia" can be reduced to specific genetic, neurophysiological, or neuroanatomical abnormalities. Such theories may still illuminate specific processes associated with neurodevelopmental psychopathology, but they need to be considered in a more holistic context. This section begins with a discussion of the key concept of vulnerability, and then, consistent with the biosystemic paradigm, turns to specific etiological mechanisms at biological, psychological, and social levels of functioning.

2.1   The Concept of Vulnerability

Having a parent with schizophrenia increases a child's risk for the disorder tenfold

Decades before today's consensus that schizophrenia is not a discrete, singular condition, it was clear that it had no single cause. On the one hand, genealogical research has long indicated involvement of heredity. Having a parent diagnosed with schizophrenia raises a child's statistical risk from the general population rate of from about 1% or less to about 10%, even if the child is never in the care of the diagnosed parent. Having an identical twin with schizophrenia increases the risk to about 50%, even when the twins are raised separately. On the other hand, of people diagnosed, only a minority have any first-degree relatives with schizophrenia. To explain this paradox, Paul Meehl, a founding figure in clinical psychology, made a distinction between schizotaxia, schizotypy, and schizophrenia. *Schizotaxia* is the genetic component, and *schizotypy* is the hypothetical phenotype of schizotaxia that creates a *vulnerability* to actual schizophrenia. Schizotypy is a psychological construct, hypothesized to have trait-like properties, measurable by instruments like the Minnesota Multiphasic Personality Inventory (MMPI) and numerous self-report scales developed specifically for that purpose. Only a minority of people (about 10%) with schizotaxia and schizotypy are expected to actually develop schizophrenia, suggesting that the genetic vulnerability must interact with something else, perhaps environmental, to produce the disorder.

In the mid-1970s Joseph Zubin, another seminal figure in clinical psychology, and his student Bonnie Spring proposed that vulnerability is *fundamental* to understanding the etiology of schizophrenia. *Diathesis*, an older medical term similar in meaning to vulnerability, began to reappear in the literature, and the leading theory of schizophrenia became known as the *diathesis-stress model*. There was a major shift in psychopathology research, a new focus on abnormalities not only in people diagnosed with schizophrenia but also their biological relatives, and in children thought to be at risk, mostly because their parent had been diagnosed.

A focus on vulnerabilities was seen as antithetical to the neo-Kraepelinian emphasis on symptoms and diagnosis, and the neo-Kraepelinian era, which also began in the 1970s, was inhospitable to vulnerability research. As neo-Kraepelinian influence waned, vulnerability research accelerated. By the end of the 20th century multiple abnormalities had been identified – in the domains of attention, perception, language, and motor functioning – that are present in individuals with hereditary risk for schizophrenia and in the case of children, that statistically predict later onset of illness. In addition, some childhood disorders, e.g., intellectual disability (mental retardation in older terminologies), attention deficit hyperactivity disorder (ADHD), and autism, are also associated with a heightened probability of schizophrenia in adulthood. Research also began to address another paradox not addressed by the Meehl-Zubin perspective: The vulnerability is not specific to schizophrenia. It generalizes beyond schizophrenia to other psychiatric disorders, even alcoholism. This realization led to our current concepts of neurodevelopmental disorders and the schizophrenia spectrum.

Psychological abnormalities hypothesized to be hereditary vulnerabilities for mental illness came to be known as *endophenotypes*, phenotypes observable only through special methods (e.g., psychological tests). Today much of the research on the etiology of the schizophrenia spectrum involves a search for endophenotypes, although it is no longer presumed that all psychological vulnerabilities have genetic origins. Consistent with the biosystemic paradigm of modern behavioral neuroscience (see Section 1.1.4), vulnerabilities are identified at genetic, neurophysiological, neuropsychological, cognitive, behavioral and social levels of functioning. The research now generally addresses two key questions:

1. What are the abnormalities that make a person vulnerable to a schizophrenia spectrum disorder and where do they come from?
2. How do vulnerabilities interact to produce the diagnosed disorder?

2.2 Genetics

Before development of modern genomic methods, almost all of what was known about the genetics of the schizophrenia spectrum was inferred from genealogical analysis, which is based on inheritance of traits in families. It works to consider some diseases "traits" for the purpose of genealogical analysis, e.g., amyotrophic lateral sclerosis (ALS, Lou Gehrig's Disease). However, the diagnostic category "schizophrenia" is not sufficiently trait-like for this purpose because it has so many variable features. Unsurprisingly, the limited conclusion from the genetic trait research was that genes are definitely involved in schizophrenia, in fact, many of them, interacting and exerting their effects in myriad ways. In retrospect, the data were also trying to tell us that schizophrenia is not a specific disease.

With the advent of modern genomic methods and the insights associated with vulnerability, neurodevelopmental disorders, and the schizophrenia spectrum genetic research is better able to identify links between specific genes and endophenotypes suspected of being vulnerabilities for the disorder. In research using animal models of disorders, methods include eliminating or disabling specific genes, "knock-out" or "knock-down" methods, allowing experimental analysis of the developmental consequences of gene dysfunction. In research on humans, genomic methods are used in conjunction with psychological measures and advanced brain imaging methods to observe the consequences of naturally occurring variations in specific genes.

Research on the *COMT gene* provides a paradigmatic example of how our understanding of genetic vulnerabilities is progressing. COMT directs biosynthesis of *catechol-O-methyltransferase*, an enzyme that regulates catecholamine neurotransmitters. Humans sometimes experience COMT dysfunction as a *deletion syndrome*, caused by loss of segments of chromosomes during cellular reproduction. People with a particular deletion syndrome only have one copy of the COMT gene per cell, and the result is abnormal metabolism of catecholamine neurotransmitters. This abnormality is statistically associated with higher incidence of a range of psychiatric problems and diagnoses, including those in the schizophrenia spectrum.

COMT is also suspected to contribute to vulnerability via *polymorphisms*, variants of a specific gene. COMT polymorphisms create structural variations in the methyltransferase enzyme, which in turn alters neurotransmitter metabolism. As with COMT deletion, some COMT polymorphisms are associated with a range of psychiatric problems, including schizophrenia spectrum disorders. However, both variants occur in normal populations, and although they produce differences in brain activation patterns, these do not necessarily lead to cognitive or behavioral deficits. COMT has been linked to histological abnormalities (i.e., abnormal cell structure) in the prefrontal cortex in subjects diagnosed with schizophrenia, but findings have been inconsistent and difficult to interpret. Despite many intriguing findings, we understand little about the role of COMT in schizophrenia spectrum vulnerability.

The genetics of schizophrenia are not fully understood

Research on gene polymorphisms as vulnerability factors has produced over 100 candidate genes. So far, none of them are better understood than COMT. An alternative research strategy has evolved, looking beyond individual polymorphisms, using quantitative measures of an individual's overall genetic risk (Meier et al., 2016). Also, consistent with the neurodevelopmental disorder concept, research has broadened to include genes that direct brain *development* in childhood and adolescence (e.g., Proenca et al., 2011). New approaches are increasingly able to address interactions between genes, cognition, and other factors (e.g., Walton et al., 2014), but it appears that the genetic contribution to vulnerability is extremely complex and will require much further research to unravel.

2.3   Theories Involving Viruses or Immunopathology

The search for acquired vulnerabilities, i.e., ones not produced by genes, has included viruses and *inflammation*, a physiological response to infection or damage. Biological markers of *immune system over-activation* are elevated in people with schizophrenia. These markers include certain *cytokines* (proteins that perform a communication function in the immune system), inflammatory agents, anti-inflammatory agents, and antibodies (proteins that attack foreign substances). Inflammation can affect brain function through the activation of *microglia*, cells that perform immunological functions in the CNS, and other mechanisms. Microglia activation (which, if excessive can lead to destruction of healthy neurons) is elevated and is related to positive symptom expression in people at high risk for psychosis. There is an increased risk of hospitalization for infectious disease in the years prior to a first episode of psychosis, further evidence of immunological dysfunction. Anti-inflammatory pharmacological agents (e.g., celecoxib, aspirin, minocycline, fish oil high in omega-3 fatty acids) may reduce psychotic symptoms, consistent with their effects in promoting recovery from traumatic brain injury.

Convergent findings suggest that sustained maternal immune system activation during pregnancy causes alterations in fetal brain development that increase risk for schizophrenia in the child. Anything that triggers prolonged immune system activation may increase risk for schizophrenia. In addition to microglial activation, viral exposure can also alter dopamine, serotonin, and glutamate levels in the brain, changes that are also related to schizophrenia. This may account for a season-of-birth effect. People whose second trimester was during winter months in temperate climates (the flu season) have an elevated risk for adult schizophrenia.

Prolonged immune system activation increases one's risk for schizophrenia

The evidence for immune system activation in schizophrenia is consistent with the vulnerability or diathesis-stress model. Abnormal fetal brain development caused by maternal infection during pregnancy is the diathesis, whereas infection in adolescence or early adulthood could be the stressor that precipitates the disorder. Key challenges for future work are to determine if immune factors map onto specific subtypes of patients and to see if inflammatory markers can aid in diagnosis and treatment.

Related to hypotheses of infection or inflammation during gestation is the hypothesis that extreme environmental stress may also cause dysplasia, possibly through the toxic effects of the hormone cortisol crossing the placenta and entering the fetal brain (Walker and Diforio, 1997). This hypothesis is supported at the epidemiological level, by the finding that in the Netherlands, individuals born after the German invasion at the outset of World War II showed an increase in incidence of schizophrenia over epidemiological base rates (van Os & Selten, 1998).

2.4   Birth Complications

Pregnancy complications, hypoxia, and low birth weight all lead to vulnerability for schizophrenia spectrum disorders

Birth complications are another possible origin of vulnerabilities and disruption of neurodevelopment. Three types of difficulties are related to an increased rate of developing the disorder: pregnancy complications (e.g., bleeding, incompatibility of immunological factors such as Rh), delivery complications (e.g., hypoxia), and/or abnormal fetal development (e.g., low birth weight, reduced head size). The causes of these problems could be completely unrelated to mental illness, but any could disrupt normal neurodevelopment, leading to vulnerability for schizophrenia spectrum disorders.

2.5   Neuroanatomy

Disrupted neurodevelopment can cause abnormalities in neuroanatomy, observable at the cellular level in post mortem brains. Even before the advent of advanced brain imaging technology, it was known that people with schizophrenia sometimes have abnormal orientation of neurons in the hippocampus, a brain structure often implicated in schizophrenia spectrum disorders. Hippocampal damage has been implicated in a variety of psychotic phenomena, including decontextualizing of memories and alterations of self-experience, both of which are common in schizophrenia. Similar hippocampal alterations have been observed in abused children, which may account for the high incidence of childhood abuse and neglect among people with schizophrenia spectrum disorders.

At least some neuroanatomical abnormalities associated with the schizophrenia spectrum are thought to be the result of *neurodysplasia*, disruption of the processes by which brain cells migrate from their embryonic origins to their adult locations and structures. Neurodysplasia may also account for some dysfunctions of frontal cortical neurons, at least in part, possibly contributing to negative symptoms after onset as well as vulnerability. The dysplasia may be caused by the genetic, infectious, stress-related, and traumatic factors discussed in the previous sections.

Earlier theories localizing schizophrenia symptoms to single brain structures are giving way to more complex models of interactions between regions. The regions most implicated in such theories are the frontal lobes, the temporal lobes, and the basal ganglia. The cerebellum, thalamus, and hippocampus also play significant roles. Alterations in thalamic activity are associated with disturbed integration of mental activity. Similarly, an alteration in cerebellar functioning could produce *dysmetria*, a disturbance of signal timing, analogous to a computer's CPU clock signal, in pathways involving the cortex, thalamus, and cerebellum. The dysmetria theory can account for a range of symptoms and cognitive deficits in schizophrenia, although it lacks specificity and has not been experimentally tested.

Dysmetria is one type of impairment in *cognitive coordination*, coordination of information processing across brain areas. This will be discussed in greater detail in Section 2.8. In addition to neurodysplasia, impairments in cognitive coordination could be caused by excessive neuronal pruning and reduced dendritic branching in adolescence, or by neurophysiological abnormalities independent of anatomy.

2.6   Neurophysiology

At the neurophysiological level of biosystemic functioning, etiological theories have tended to focus more on the proximal causes of the diagnosed disorder and its symptoms rather than vulnerabilities. Nevertheless, the bridges between genetics and neurophysiology are evolving rapidly in current developmental neuroscience, and the near future will see models that integrate genetic and nongenetic neurodevelopmental vulnerability with the neurophysiology of the disorder itself.

Neurophysiological models of schizophrenia most often involve the neurotransmitter *dopamine* and its receptors, especially the *D2 receptor*. This has grown out of several lines of evidence, including: (1) the occurrence of psychotic symptoms in people who abuse amphetamines, cocaine, and other drugs known to increase brain dopamine activity; (2) emergence of psychotic symptoms in Parkinson's disease patients who receive excessive doses of L-dopa, a metabolic precursor of dopamine; and (3) the effects of *antipsychotic drug*s, all of which are dopamine antagonists or partial agonists at the D2 receptor (among many other actions). Studies of dopamine metabolites in the spinal fluid of patients, or from postmortem studies, do not consistently support a simple model of excessive amounts of dopamine, however. Blocking the D2 receptor does reduce dopamine transmission and has a proximal effect on positive psychotic symptoms, but this still may be secondary or "downstream" from other neurophysiological origins of psychosis.

> **Most neurophysiological models of schizophrenia implicate dopamine and the D2 receptor**

For example, dopamine dysregulation could be a secondary "downstream" effect of *glutamate system dysregulation*, also implicated in schizophrenia. The glutamate system is the most widely distributed in the cortex, the "workhorse of the brain" that supports basic information processing. As the primary excitatory neurotransmitter, glutamate interacts extensively with *gamma-aminobutyric acid* (GABA), the primary inhibitory neurotransmitter. Abnormal interactions between the GABA system and the *n-methyl–d-aspartate* (NMDA) glutamate receptor could account for the widespread cognitive coordination disturbances in schizophrenia described in Section 2.8. NMDA dysfunction is implicated in electrophysiological abnormalities observed in the schizophrenia spectrum, e.g., reduced amplitude of the *mismatch negativity* wave in the evoked response paradigm, thought to reflect a fundamental component of executive cognition. Plausible genetic origins of NMDA receptor dysfunction have been proposed (Schwartz, Sachdeva, & Stahl, 2012). However, a complete understanding of glutamate dysfunction in the schizophrenia spectrum remains elusive.

Interaction of the glutamate and dopamine systems has been proposed in models of acute onset and psychotic episodes. In *corticofugal models of psychosis*, frontal dopamine projections perform an alarm function on prefrontal glutamate systems, activating information processing needed to confront the threat that tripped the alarm. Normally, glutaminergic activity leads to inhibition of the dopamine system for a return to baseline levels. However, frontal glutamate hypoactivation would lead to decreased activation of inhibitory interneurons, and without the negative feedback loop the dopamine system accelerates to a point of widespread disruption. The frontal hypoactivation could account for negative symptoms and persistent cognitive vulnerabilities, while the dopamine hyperactivity could account for acute psychosis. The failure to activate frontal systems was first thought to be due to embryonic neuro-dysplasia, but NMDA receptor dysfunction could produce a comparable result. Though plausible, corticofugal models have not been experimentally tested.

Dopamine, serotonin, glutamate, and GABA have all been implicated in patients with schizophrenia

Another neurotransmitter implicated in schizophrenia is *serotonin*. In the 1950s and 1960s research studies and clinical observations on the emergence of psychotic symptoms following administration of LSD, mescaline, and other drugs known to increase serotonergic activity suggested a link between serotonin and the schizophrenia spectrum. However, the relationship is not a simple one. Like glutamate and GABA, serotonin and dopamine interact in complex regulatory mechanisms. Pharmacological alteration of one will affect the other, in different ways in different parts of the system. For example, action at the *5HT2A receptor*, a serotonin receptor that regulates dopaminergic neurons, appears to play a role in the lack of extrapyramidal side effects of atypical antipsychotics. Although the serotonin system appears to play a complex role in psychosis, and although some antipsychotic drugs act on serotonin receptors, blockade or partial agonism of the D2 receptor remains a *sine qua non* of antipsychotic drugs. Much more research is needed to understand the role of the serotonin system in schizophrenia spectrum etiology.

Like the retreat from localized neuroanatomical origins, neurophysiological findings increasingly indicate that *interactions* among neurotransmitter systems are important for understanding the schizophrenia spectrum. For example, *phencyclidine* (PCP) and *ketamine* both can produce psychosis in normal subjects. They both cause reduction of NMDA receptor activity and also increased metabolic turnover of dopamine, both of which are associated with schizophrenia. In addition, alterations in neurotransmitter functioning can result from pregnancy, obstetric complications, stress, trauma, drug use, and genetic abnormalities. New developments in the psychopharmacology of schizophrenia also involve a focus on multiple neurotransmitter systems. Thus, whereas first-generation antipsychotic medications (e.g., *haloperidol, chlorpromazine*) were chosen for their ability to block dopamine receptors, newer drugs often target multiple systems, including dopamine, glutamate, serotonin, and norepinephrine (see Section 4.2 on Mechanisms of Action).

In *computational psychiatry*, mathematical relationships between neurophysiological processes are represented by computer models (Friston, Stephan, Montague, & Dolan, 2014). These models can be developed and tested in computers much more rapidly than in animals. The models can represent ways that various neurotransmitter systems, other dimensions of neurophysiology, and the physical configuration of neurons, dendrites, and synapses, can interact to perform information processing functions. At least some of the cognitive impairments of schizophrenia spectrum disorders can be understood as "downstream" consequences of failures in the neuronal mechanisms captured by such models (e.g., Lewis & Glausier, 2016).

2.7 Neurodevelopmental Factors

The neurodevelopmental ideas that dominate contemporary schizophrenia spectrum research had their origin in more specific theories of how abnormalities in infancy, childhood, and adolescence develop into the adult disorder. An influential perspective on this was contributed by Fish (1987), who identified a number of developmental abnormalities in high-risk children, naming the syndrome *pandysmaturation*. In an especially influential study, Walker (1994) used family home movies to show that trained observers could predict which children would develop a schizophrenia spectrum disorder as adults, based on the appearance of abnormal motor and postural behavior. The delayed onset of schizophrenia, mysterious for a disorder with such extensive genetic involvement, came to be understood in developmental terms. Comparisons were drawn with neuropathological disorders like cerebral palsy, which manifests as seizures, motor impairments, or cognitive impairments, depending on age and stage of brain development. As normal adolescent brain development came to be more deeply understood, the onset of schizophrenia came to be understood increasingly in terms of environmental demands on developing frontocortical systems. This has been tempered somewhat by evidence of distributed processing abnormalities (discussed in the previous section) that suggest even more basic impairments in the dynamic formation of neural networks. Disruption of complex cycles of neuronal and synaptic proliferation and pruning in adolescence may also contribute to distributed impairments (Thormodsen et al., 2013). Insights into normal adolescent development of social cognition and emotion regulation, often disrupted by vulnerabilities and actual psychosis, increasingly contributes to our understanding of the persistence of impairments between psychotic episodes.

Trained observers could predict which children in old home movies would develop schizophrenia spectrum disorders by adulthood

2.8 Cognitive Factors

Yet another founding figure in clinical psychology, David Shakow, is credited for ushering in the modern era of *experimental psychopathology*. In a psychology laboratory on the grounds of a state psychiatric hospital in the 1930s, Shakow used the methods of the time to begin building our understanding of the cognitive etiology of the schizophrenia spectrum. Decades before the emergence of modern neuropsychology, using a simple reaction time task, Shakow developed a theory of cognitive deficit in schizophrenia, *segmental set*, that foreshadowed later understanding of executive functioning impairment.

Until the mid-1960s experimental psychopathology sought to identify cognitive impairments as causing or resulting from "schizophrenia." This practice ended abruptly when psychopathologists Loren and Jean Chapman issued a series of methodological critiques revealing fatal flaws in experimental designs. Ironically, the problems the Chapmans identified were about quantitative psychometric methods (e.g., how differences between tasks in difficulty level and reliability could create the false impression that schizophrenia patients had a specific deficit in one process but not another), not the validity of the schizophrenia construct itself. The methodological solutions the Chapmans prescribed were mostly impractical, and were overtaken decades later by the realization that *any* experiment that uses diagnosis as an independent variable has serious limitations. For whatever reasons, since the Chapmans' devastating critiques, experimental psychopathologists have avoided simple comparisons of diagnostic groups and instead have sought to understand specific cognitive, neuropsychological, neurophysiological, genetic, behavioral, and social factors that contribute to specific vulnerabilities and impairments, across the schizophrenia spectrum and beyond.

In the 1990s, clinical and experimental *neuropsychology* exerted broad influence on cognitive theories of the schizophrenia spectrum (also discussed in Section 1.1.3). As neuropsychological models evolved, derivative views of cognitive impairment in schizophrenia progressed from a relatively simplistic view of "schizophrenia as frontal lobe dementia" to advanced models that incorporate multiple levels of biosystemic functioning. Neuropsychological models converged with those evolving in experimental psychopathology and behavioral and cognitive neuroscience.

The evolution of the theory of impaired *cognitive coordination* in schizophrenia provides an example of this progression. Disorganization of cognitive and behavioral functioning has long been associated with the schizophrenia spectrum. This has been demonstrated experimentally in multiple domains, originally and primarily in vision (e.g., Gestalt perception), but also in audition, memory, thought, and motor activity. For example, impairment in *pre-attentive stimulus grouping*, an automatic perceptual organization process that occurs before involvement of the executive or attention functions associated with conscious awareness, is often observed in schizophrenia. Based on consistent data indicating that reduced perceptual organization was related to reduced organization in other cognitive domains (e.g., language), it was hypothesized that all of these forms of disorganization reflect a fundamental impairment in cognitive coordination, that is, a reduced ability to modulate processing of sensory, linguistic, or mnemonic representations by spatially, temporally, or semantically-related information (either in the environment or stored in memory). For example, in the domain of language, the brain uses the larger narrative in which words occur to guide analysis of meaning. So-called *formal thought disorder* (fragmentation or derailment of language and underlying cognitive processes), a diagnostic criterion symptom for schizophrenia, can be interpreted as a weakening of the normal predictive constraints that words or ideas have on the generation of subsequent words and ideas. Impairments in coordination of cognitive activity may have a structural basis, in abnormal dendritic branching and other aspects of dendrite function. Disorganization may also be influenced by reduced lateral interactions between pyramidal cells, possibly secondary to NMDA-receptor hypofunction. While cognitive coordination impairments are ubiquitous in schizophrenia spectrum disorders, they are not universal. When present they are specifically linked to disorganized *symptoms* (Phillips, Clark, & Silverstein, 2015).

A related example is the progression of *context processing* theories, initially formulated in the early 1990s but still evolving today. Context processing is understood as an aspect of *working memory*, a memory register that contains information necessary to perform a complicated task at hand. Working memory is considered part of the executive system because executive processes continuously manipulate its contents in the course of task performance. Context processing theories of psychopathology are hybrids, as the working memory concept derives primarily from neuropsychology, while context processing derives primarily from experimental psychopathology. A single impairment at any point in interactions between executive processes, working memory, and context processing could account for poor performance on a multitude of different tasks. Reduced dopaminergic activity in the dorsolateral prefrontal cortex could provide the neurophysiological substrate of the deficit. Experiments using working memory tasks have generally supported the original theory. However, although it was originally hypothesized that a context processing deficit would be associated with negative symptoms, later studies demonstrated that it is more associated with disorganized symptoms, as predicted by the Phillips et al. (2015) cognitive coordination theory. Context processing impairments shed light on working memory deficits but do not account for deficits in spatial context processing. It is possible to integrate theories that emphasize contextual effects in perception, working memory, language, and learning via a unified model grounded in information theory (Silverstein, 2016). However, these models describe interrelationships between specific impairments and their functional impairments in the schizophrenia spectrum, not the etiology of "schizophrenia."

Context processing and cognitive coordination theories were projected into the domain of treatment by Gerard Hogarty and colleagues in Cognitive Enhancement Therapy (CET; further discussed in section 4.1.6). CET is a therapeutic approach to improving interpersonal functioning that emphasizes acquisition of rapid, holistic processing of a social situation, i.e., its *context.* Research on the role of context processing impairment in the schizophrenia spectrum plays a central role in the CET rationale. Controlled treatment trials indicate CET is effective in improving social cognition and behavioral performance, although it has not been systematically compared to other approaches that combine cognitive methods with behavioral skill training.

Cognitive Enhancement Therapy (CET) focuses on helping patients understand context in order to improve interpersonal functioning

Cognitive deficit theories do not always specify whether a deficit of interest is *vulnerability-linked* (i.e., contributes primarily to enduring vulnerability), *symptom-linked* (i.e., causing specific symptoms), *episode-linked* (i.e., involved with onset, or present only during acute episodes), or *episode-sensitive* (i.e., a vulnerability-linked impairment that becomes more severe during a psychotic episode). One exception is a model of episodic cognitive impairment based on the functioning of a dopamine-based probabilistic learning mechanism involving interaction between the *striatum*, a subcortical brain region, and frontal cortex (Spaulding & Nolting, 2006; further discussed in Section 2.6). In this view, response to psychological treatments targeting cognitive impairments is seen as due to reorganization of response hierarchies disrupted by acute dopamine dysregulation. Interest in the probabilistic learning mechanism has recently expanded to become a fairly comprehensive model of cognitive impairment in the schizophrenia spectrum (Strauss, Whearty, Frost, & Carpenter, 2016), but its role in episodic psychosis remains untested.

In summary, cognitive theories of schizophrenia, like theories associated with the other levels of biosystemic functioning, have proliferated over the past decade and have increasingly reflected the sophistication of modern cognitive and behavioral neuroscience. New terms have been introduced to distinguish between types of cognitive models, e.g., *neurocognition* and *social cognition*, although such distinctions are heuristic and do not necessarily reflect natural categories. The proliferation reflects in part our new view of schizophrenia as a spectrum with multiple, partially independent etiologies that produce specific *features* of vulnerability or the actual disorder in myriad combinations. The theories no longer compete to explain a single disorder. Increasingly, they can be understood as complementary, accounting for different aspects of a very complex and heterogeneous type of mental illness.

2.9   Social Learning Theory

Modern *social learning theory* has figured heavily in development of psychiatric rehabilitation and its various methods and techniques, yet it has not been used to formulate etiological theories of the schizophrenia spectrum, arguably with isolated exceptions (e.g., Heilbrun, 1973). This is partly because social learning theory does not assume diagnostic categories or mental illnesses. Instead, the key principle is that any aspect of personal or social function can potentially be learned or unlearned (i.e., extinguished). The impairments of mental illness can thus be potentially viewed as reflecting the absence of skills, which can be taught and reinforced, or the past reinforcement of behaviors which are generally socially *in*appropriate, and which can be eliminated via extinction and response cost procedures. This principle has made social learning theory a critical tool in the clinical psychologist's toolbox for virtually all domains of mental health and illness. The skill principle is especially complementary to the goals and methods of psychiatric rehabilitation (see Section 1.1.5).

In a landmark conceptual synthesis, Kurt Salzinger (1973, 1984) identified the interface between learning theories and etiological theories of schizophrenia in his *immediacy hypothesis*. The immediacy hypothesis states that the behavioral impairments of schizophrenia all stem from an impairment that causes all behavior to be controlled by stimulus conditions that are more immediate, or temporally proximal to the behavior, than would normally be the case. This accounted for the remarkable success of treatment approaches based on learning principles, i.e., token economies (Ayllon & Azrin, 1968). Token economies make the antecedents and consequences of behavior more immediate and more consistent, thus putting them within the apprehension abilities of people with an immediacy deficit. As social learning theory incorporated classical and operant learning in its mental health applications, the insights of the immediacy hypothesis pervasively (if implicitly) influenced design of therapeutic environments and development of behavioral treatments (e.g., Paul & Lentz, 1977).

Today we recognize immediacy to reflect an important dimension of psychological development. Children function in a time frame defined by the influence of reinforcement and punishment on their behavior, and this gradually lengthens to the adult time frame over the course of development. Immediacy has converged with the neuropsychological constructs of attention and executive functioning and is a central component of current theories of attention deficit hyperactivity disorder (ADHD), another neurodevelopmental disorder linked to the schizophrenia spectrum (Daly, Hildenbrand, Brown, 2016; see Section 1.6.1). Further convergences of social learning theory and cognitive and behavioral neuroscience will have an important role in new insights about etiology, as well as new treatment and rehabilitation methods, in the foreseeable future.

2.10   Environmental Factors

The past decade has seen intensive research on the role of environmental factors, such as adverse childhood experiences, on long-term health (e.g., Monnat & Chandler, 2015). Several forms of environmental stress and/or trauma may be involved in creating schizophrenia spectrum vulnerabilities. Neglect, abuse, and other trauma during childhood are associated with increased rates of adult schizophrenia, and high rates of neglect and physical and sexual abuse are found in the histories of people with schizophrenia. There is some evidence that it is maternal physical abuse that creates the critical vulnerability (Fisher et al., 2010). Emotional neglect is associated with cognitive disorganization and decreased gray matter volume in adults with schizophrenia (Cancel et al., 2015). Abuse is also related to poorer premorbid functioning and to decreased cognitive functioning, although such effects are not specific to the schizophrenia spectrum (Berthelot et al., 2015). The effects may be moderated by genetic vulnerability, e.g., polymorphisms of the serotonin transporter gene (Aas et al., 2012).

> **High rates of childhood neglect and physical and sexual abuse are found in people with schizophrenia**

As discussed in Section 1.3, stress leading to vulnerability for schizophrenia spectrum disorder could be generated by interactions of poverty, cultural context, and local community factors. These environmental stressors can also affect gene expression in a type of interaction known as epigenetic regulation. This can then further influence the expression of vulnerabilities, symptoms, and other impairments in adults.

Urban birth, urban upbringing, and migration to urban areas within a person's country of origin are also strongly related to an increased risk for schizophrenia. These findings cannot be accounted for by increased drug use, or by a tendency for mentally ill people to migrate to urban areas. An intriguing possibility is that the effect of urban environments on schizophrenia is mediated by exposure to a virus. For example, some evidence suggests exposure to viruses or other microorganisms (e.g., *toxoplasmosis gondii,* a food- and water-borne parasite) may create vulnerability (see also section 2.3 above on viral and immunological factors).

International migration is associated with increased risk for schizophrenia (Werbeloff, Levine, & Rabinowitz, 2012). The findings are strongest for people migrating from developing countries to developed countries and for people of black skin color. Among migrating populations, rates of schizophrenia are significantly higher than among the native populations of the countries from which people migrated. There is a lower incidence of schizophrenia when nonwhite ethnic minorities live in areas where minorities make up a large

> **Urban living and international migration are both associated with increased risk for schizophrenia**

proportion of the local population. This evidence suggests that the long-term experience of social defeat and stress associated with being an underprivileged minority, immigrant, or other cultural outsider, is the causative mechanism. Evidence also comes from animal studies where social defeat leads to increased dopamine levels in the nucleus accumbens and prefrontal cortex, regions relevant to schizophrenia. As with abuse, chronic severe stress may produce biological, including epigenetic, changes that, in combination with other psychological and biological factors, produce symptoms and impairments.

Exposure to illicit substances of abuse is arguably an environmental etiological factor. Cannabis use in adolescents increases risk for a schizophrenia spectrum disorder, probably through complex interactions between genetic vulnerabilities and neurodevelopment (French et al., 2015). Cannabis affects people with vulnerabilities differently than healthy controls (Epstein & Kumra, 2014), but neurodevelopmental effects in the adolescent brain are sufficient reason to discourage its use before adulthood regardless of vulnerability. It is unclear whether cannabis affects the course after onset (Power et al., 2015).

3

Diagnosis and Treatment Indications

3.1 Assessment

3.1.1 Neurophysiological and Symptom Assessment

There is no practical technology for clinically assessing the neurophysiological status of schizophrenia spectrum disorders. Portable electroencephalography (EEG) and magnetoencephalography (MEG) devices have recently been developed, and these will eventually allow for low cost assessment of regional and integrative brain activity, and so we expect these to eventually be useful for schizophrenia spectrum disorders. Low-cost or portable functional brain imaging has not yet been developed. In the distant future, genomic assessments may prove helpful in selecting individualized medication regimens. Meanwhile, neurophysiological status must be inferred from systematic assessment of psychotic symptoms, cognitive functioning, and longitudinal changes in the patient's personal and social functioning. Precise description of the quality, frequency, and intensity of symptoms can guide the choice of pharmacologic and behavioral methods targeted at symptom reduction. It is important to note, however, that response to treatment of symptoms is relatively independent of response to treatment of other targets, e.g., cognitive impairments. Symptom assessment alone is therefore insufficient as an assessment strategy for the schizophrenia spectrum, where many other areas of potential disability (e.g., social and instrumental role functioning) will affect long-term prognosis. Unfortunately, due to the poor dissemination of psychiatric rehabilitation, in many settings assessment and treatment are limited to psychotic symptoms.

A number of interview-based symptom rating scales are used widely in research (reviewed by Silverstein, 2000). One, the Brief Psychiatric Rating Scale, is sometimes used in clinical practice and has been incorporated in a computerized clinical decision support system (Young, Mintz, Cohen, & Chinman, 2004). These measures are clinically useful for assessing symptom change over time, especially response to medication.

3.1.2 Cognitive Assessment

Depending on the study, specific measures and settings, some 50–95% of people with schizophrenia spectrum disorders fall outside the normal range on at least one domain of neuropsychological or related cognitive assessments. There is no unique or "signature" cognitive impairment profile of any particu-

Most people with schizophrenia spectrum disorders will show some neuropsychological impairment

lar diagnosis and no specific impairment that is found in only one diagnostic group. However, the prognostic significance of the overall degree of neuropsychological impairment during stable, non-acute periods is indisputable – more severe impairment predicts poorer long-term outcome.

In the 1970s computerized laboratory assessment of cognition began to appear. In the 1980s computerized test batteries specialized for the schizophrenia spectrum were in use, with specific measures derived from experimental psychopathology (Spaulding, Crinean, & Martin, 1983). In the 1990s such batteries had become components of comprehensive clinical decision support systems, feeding information on patients' cognitive functioning to the treatment teams in high intensity psychiatric rehabilitation programs (Spaulding, Fleming, Sullivan, Storzbach, & Lam, 1999). Also in the 1990s, the insight that schizophrenia spectrum disorders are in a sense neuropsychological disorders led to development of non-computerized batteries derived from neuropsychological measures, e.g., the Repeatable Battery for the Neuropsychological Assessment of Schizophrenia (RBANS; Hobart, Goldberg, Bartko, & Gold, 1999) and the Brief Assessment of Cognition in Schizophrenia (BACS; Keefe et al., 2004).

At the turn of the 21st century, in response to the need for a standardized battery for schizophrenia spectrum research, the National Institute of Mental Health (NIMH) sponsored the Measurement and Treatment Research to Improve Cognition in Schizophrenia (MATRICS) project. This culminated in the MATRICS Consensus Cognitive Battery (MCCB; August, Kiwanuka, McMahon, & Gold, 2012). The MCCB was especially intended to illuminate the nature of drug actions on cognitive functioning. It is too early, however, to determine whether availability of the MCCB will influence drug development or clinical assessment. For the time being, the most extensive discussion of how cognitive measures support the clinical assessment of schizophrenia spectrum disorders is in the neuropsychological literature (Marcopulos & Kurtz, 2012). That discussion suggests cognitive measures play important roles in determining severity of disability, identifying areas of strength and weakness and need for environmental supports, predicting treatment response, and informing issues involving risk, forensic status, and disposition.

With progress in the move towards a recovery orientation, there has been an increased emphasis on patient reports of their own cognitive challenges. Interest in this led to development of the Schizophrenia Cognition Rating Scale (SCoRS) (Keefe et al., 2015), an interview-based measure. The SCoRS is a reliable and valid measure that is also sensitive to treatment effects on cognition. However, self-report of cognitive difficulty does not correlate highly with performance on laboratory tests of neuropsychological functioning or in vivo functioning. Consistent with recovery principles, both subjective and objective domains of cognitive functioning must be assessed.

3.1.3   Dynamic Assessment

Most traditional cognitive and functional measures can be viewed as forms of *static assessment* in the sense that they measure the skills a person has at any given moment, as opposed to what they are capable of learning and therefore of a person's potential ability. This issue has been faced earlier in other areas, such as intelligence testing, and has led the development of methods of *dynamic* or *learning potential assessment*, focusing on the ability to change performance under instructional or learning conditions.

The Micro-Module Learning Test (MMLT; Silverstein, Wallace, & Schenkel, 2005) is a pragmatic, face-valid instrument for dynamic assessment. It provides a brief measure of responsiveness to the three core components involved in skills training: verbal instruction, modeling, and role-play (further discussed in Section 4.1.6 and 4.1.7). It has seven psychometrically equivalent alternate forms to facilitate repeated testing for longitudinal assessment. The MMLT was developed, in part, because there was a need for a relatively brief and accurate assessment tool that would predict a patient's performance before being placed in a skills training intervention, which often lasts from 3 to 6 months. While successful prediction of performance in skills training has been achieved using traditional neuropsychological measures, an assumption driving the development of the MMLT was that by using the basic structure and content found in skills training procedures, greater ecological and predictive validity would be achieved. With the MMLT, clinicians can determine whether a patient is ready to benefit from a skill-training group or whether preliminary interventions are required.

3.1.4   Functional Assessment

Over the past two decades, as psychiatric rehabilitation has become a comprehensive paradigm, a number of instruments have been developed to provide the information needed to use its methods and accomplish its goals. This began with literature reviews and consensus conferences of stakeholders of mental health services that have developed criteria for functional assessment instruments (e.g., IAPSRS, 1997; Menditto, et al., 1999). Characteristics of these newer measures include: (1) the ability to assess, in both inpatient and outpatient settings, functioning in the types of roles characteristic of people with serious mental illnesses; (2) the inclusion of information from multiple sources; (3) a focus on strengths and skills rather than on deficits and symptoms; (4) assessment of a wide range of skills relevant for successful community living; (5) an easy to administer format; (6) established reliability and validity; and (7) an ease of translating the findings into a rehabilitation plan (Menditto et al., 1999). Some of the measures apply the skill principle of social learning theory, conceptualizing the domains being measured as learnable skills. Also, some incorporate recovery principles, including in the scope of measurement a person's individual desires, interests, aspirations, goals, values, and subjective experience.

One such measure is the Client's Assessment of Strength, Interests, and Goals (CASIG; Wallace, Lecomte, Wilde, & Liberman, 2001). The CASIG is administered as a structured interview that begins by eliciting the individual's medium-term goals in five areas of community living: housing, money/work, interpersonal relationships, health, and spiritual activities. Follow-up questions clarify these domain-specific goals and ask the patient to specify to the best of their ability the services needed to achieve them. The rest of the

CASIG involves questions assessing current and past community functioning, medication compliance and side effects, quality of life, quality of treatment, symptoms, and performance of intolerable community behaviors.

Another useful measure is the Independent Living Skills Inventory (ILSI) (Menditto et al., 1999). The ILSI measures a person's ability to perform a range of skills needed for successful community living. A unique feature of the scale is that each item is rated along two dimensions. One is how much of the skill can be performed, and the other is the degree of assistance required to perform the complete skill. This scoring method is useful in planning a rehabilitation program because it distinguishes between skill deficits and performance deficits, each requiring different forms of intervention. The ILSI has eleven subscales, each representing a different domain of community functioning (e.g., money management, home maintenance, cooking, etc.). The ILSI can be efficiently completed based on historical and interview data and has high face-validity making it relatively user-friendly.

A potential problem with self-report based measures of behavioral functioning is that patients with severe cognitive impairment, thought disorganization, and/or delusional thinking may provide inaccurate information. Similarly, for measures like the ILSI that depend on key informants, such informants may be unavailable, or the client may not have been in settings where the relevant skill could be demonstrated. Assessments that incorporate role-playing and related techniques can sometimes provide more reliable information about specific skills. For example, the UCSD Performance-Based Skills Assessment (UPSA) (Patterson, Goldman, McKibbin, Hughs & Jeste, 2001) uses role-playing and task performance in a laboratory setting to assess skills in the areas of household chores, communication, finance, transportation, and planning recreational activities. Such assessments provide more detailed and reliable information than self-report and historical instruments, but they are inevitably narrower in scope because of the time and cost required for administration.

Social skills training is a critical component in almost all social learning programs

Role-playing is critical to reliable assessment of social or interpersonal skills. Social skills training, an iconic treatment modality in psychiatric rehabilitation, has role playing-based assessment of interpersonal skills built into it. The Maryland Assessment of Social Competence (MASC; Bellack, Brown, & Thomas-Loorman, 2006) is a free-standing instrument that uses comparable techniques to measure the ability to resolve interpersonal problems through conversation. The MASC has alternative forms to facilitate repeated measurement and longitudinal assessment of change, an important feature when acquisition of social skill is a key rehabilitation and recovery goal.

For people with the most severe impairments and disabilities being treated in intensive, longer-term residential settings, observational assessment systems have a critical role in assessment and treatment. One of these measures is the Time Sample Behavioral Checklist (TSBC; Paul, 1987), an observational measure of the frequency of a range of appropriate and inappropriate behaviors. TSBC observations are made on a regular schedule during all waking hours for all patients in a residential treatment program, yielding a weekly average of about 100 observations per person. These observations allow a treatment team to track behaviors as specific as frequency of social interaction, bizarre behavior, facial expression, and many others. A complementary measure developed by Paul and colleagues is the Clinical

Frequencies Recording System (CFRS; Paul & Lentz, 1977). This is also an observational scale, but it uses event-sampling procedures to record the occurrence of event-specific behaviors such as attendance and successful participation in groups as well as of low-frequency clinically critical behaviors (e.g., aggressive outbursts).

The third key measure developed as part of the Paul and Lentz (1977) project is the Staff-Resident Interaction Chronograph (SRIC; Paul, 1988). Data for the SRIC is recorded by non-interactive observers on the unit, using stratified time-sampling techniques similar to those used with the TSBC. The purpose of the SRIC is to obtain data on the nature of staff–patient interactions. SRIC data can be used to monitor adherence of staff to prescribed therapeutic behaviors as well as to evaluate entire treatment programs. The TSBC, CFRS, and SRIC have all demonstrated excellent psychometric characteristics, and have been successfully disseminated to treatment programs other than where they were developed. Together, these instruments can form the backbone of a data-driven *clinical decision support system* (Buican, Spaulding, Gordon, & Hindman, 1999) in a residential treatment program.

Integrated use of instruments like the TSBC, CFRS, and SRIC represent the *gold standard* of assessment in intensive settings that treat people with the most severe disabilities and/or the highest risks to self or others. These are usually institutional settings, e.g., the high-security units of state hospitals. In settings where people with lower levels of risk are treated, the high cost (which includes significant, continuing staff training costs) may be more difficult to justify. Intermediate-secure programs using less extensive but also less costly assessment systems have been developed (e.g., Silverstein et al., 2006; Spaulding et al., 2003), are equally compatible with comprehensive clinical decision support systems, and have comparably positive outcomes (further discussed in Section 3.2).

Comprehensive assessment will require the integrated use of multiple measures

3.2   Treatment Planning

Systematic treatment planning is a *sine qua non* in modern psychiatric rehabilitation. There are five reasons for this:

1. Schizophrenia spectrum disorders are complex combinations of relatively separate problems, each requiring its own assessment and treatment, selected from a rapidly expanding array of instruments and modalities.
2. Circumstances often dictate that problems must be addressed in a particular sequence.
3. Recovery is nevertheless a holistic process, and separate interventions for separate problems must be delivered in an integrated, coordinated manner.
4. No one practitioner has the ability to provide comprehensive psychiatric rehabilitation – it has to be done by an interdisciplinary treatment team.
5. Progress in recovery must be continuously evaluated across all problems – progress on one problem does not necessarily connote progress on others.

All this requires a formal and organized process that ensures systematic assessment of all barriers to recovery, comprehensive targeting of all relevant problems, and rigorous, objective evaluation of progress.

Comprehensive treatment planning in the schizophrenia spectrum requires attention to three classes of factors:

- The phase of the disorder;
- The behavioral deficits and excesses that require intervention and treatment;
- Needs for supportive services that can include supported education, supported housing, supported employment, financial support, case management, medical and dental care, and peer support.

Phase of the disorder refers to whether a person is in the prodromal phase of schizophrenia, the acute phase (often requiring short-term hospitalization or comparably intensive care), the post-acute stabilizing phase (i.e., with persistent symptoms and other impairments, but responding to treatment, often requiring intermediate intensity of care), or the stable baseline phase. Each of these phases requires a different treatment approach. In addition, functioning in the "stable baseline" phase may include symptoms and other impairments at virtually any level of severity, requiring any level of intensity of care.

The phase of the disorder and the setting may arguably demand different approaches to treatment planning. Hospital accreditation standards prescribe particular procedures for formulating a treatment and discharge plan, but they are rather generic, and in practice regulations are easily met without any approximation of the comprehensive and data-driven plans necessary for modern psychiatric rehabilitation. The need for comprehensiveness and systematic assessment are no greater in hospital settings than in others. Discharge from the hospital is almost always an important recovery goal, whether the setting is a short-term acute unit in a general hospital or a longer-term residential unit in a psychiatric institution. But even in non-hospital settings progression to a less restrictive, more independent living situation is usually also a recovery goal. Because of the narrower range of goals and shorter time frame, treatment in an acute hospital unit is inevitably less multimodal and in that sense less complex, but that setting has its own complexities. The challenges of managing multiple interventions across a community services system are different from, but no less demanding than, the challenges of treating severe psychosis and highly dangerous behavior in a secure setting.

3.2.1   Problem-Oriented Treatment Planning

A comprehensive approach to treatment planning and progress evaluation in psychiatric rehabilitation, based on the elements of traditional hospital treatment plans, was developed by Spaulding et al. (2003). The approach is equally suitable for a range of settings, e.g., *partial hospitalization* (a type of setting that emulates hospitalization, except that the patient goes home at night), *day programs* (similar to partial hospitalization, but somewhat less intensive and with fewer medical accouterments), longer-term *residential programs* in either community or institutional settings, and outpatient clinic settings. The key prerequisite is not the setting but the interdisciplinary team responsible for all aspects of psychiatric treatment and rehabilitation. The core feature of the approach is derived from *problem-oriented medical information systems* (PROMIS), a way of structuring clinical decision making that was pioneered in the 1960s in anticipation of today's computerized medical records systems. The treatment planning rules in the hospital accreditation standards of The Joint Commission, a major accreditor of healthcare organizations, are also derived from PROMIS.

The key feature of a PROMIS-based treatment plan is a list of functional problems, presumed to be relatively independent and requiring separate treatments, until new data suggest otherwise. Each problem is identified in a comprehensive assessment that includes both diagnostic and functional components, and associated with an operational measure that can indicate longitudinal change in the problem's severity. One or more interventions are assigned to each problem. The treatment team monitors delivery of the interventions, re-assessing and assigning new ones when expected outcomes are not achieved. Rehabilitation proceeds as an iterative process of problem resolution until no barriers to recovery goals remain. The additional features of the Spaulding et al. (2003) approach include an operationally defined set of possible problems associated with the schizophrenia spectrum and covering the full range of biosystemic levels of functioning, from neurophysiological stability to having a home, a job, and friends. Accordingly, the approach also includes rating procedures that translate the data from multiple interventions into a uniform profile of progress toward recovery goals. This profile is key to determining which interventions are producing the expected outcomes, i.e., progress toward recovery goals, and which are not.

The concept of recovery must also guide how "problems" are defined and identified in problem-oriented treatment planning. The problems most relevant are those that represent barriers to recovery. The treatment planning must therefore begin with identification of the recovering person's key goals and objectives. The barriers to achieving those goals and objectives are problems with available solutions, e.g., a barrier to having satisfying interpersonal relationships is often the problem of deficient social skills, and the solution is social skills training, social network interventions, and related modalities in the psychiatric rehabilitation toolbox. Also, a recovery orientation requires that strengths and assets be considered in the planning process as well as barriers and problems. Interrelationships between recovery goals, barriers, personal assets, problems, and solutions are a central strategic concern of psychiatric rehabilitation, and the relationships change as recovery progresses. This principle operates continuously at the level of integrated treatment teams (discussed in the next section) as well as individual modalities (e.g., in rehabilitation counseling, discussed in Section 4.1.1).

3.2.2 The Multimodal Functional Model

In data-driven evidence-based clinical practice there is no fine line between treatment planning and assessment. Problem-oriented treatment planning as elaborated by Spaulding et al. (2003) provides structure and organization that facilitates comprehensive yet efficient recovery-oriented treatment and rehabilitation services. At the same time, any such system relies in turn on a team of professionals using an array of evidence-based instruments and interventions, and systematically using the data that the array generates to make key decisions. Psychologists are generally familiar with multimodal assessment models that guide such processes. The *Multimodal Functional Model* (MFM; Hunter, Wilkniss, Gardner, & Silverstein, 2008) is one such model, developed specifically to meet the demands of psychiatric rehabilitation for the schizophrenia spectrum, and complementary to the structure of problem-oriented treatment planning.

The MFM reflects an integrated biosystemic perspective on treatment planning. In addition to incorporating data collected using standard assessment tools, the MFM also makes use of specialized data collection instruments designed for settings where fairly continuous behavioral observation is feasible. MFM proceeds in a step-wise cycle of observation, assessment, choice of treatment based on hypothesized antecedents and consequences of identified problems, and evaluation of treatment effects as in a quasi-experiment. The cycle continues until all problems posing a barrier to recovery have been neutralized.

4

Treatment

A half-century of intensive research has produced an expansive array of evidence-based treatments and related modalities for the schizophrenia spectrum. The expansiveness of the array is due to the complex, multi-problem nature of these disorders. The elements of the array are not competing approaches derived from competing theoretical perspectives. Instead, they are separate tools in a toolbox, and they must be selected for applicability to individual problems and goals on a case-by-case basis. A credible capacity for treating people with schizophrenia spectrum disorders must include access to the full array. Methods for managing this complexity are described in Section 3.2 on multimodal assessment and treatment planning. In Section 4, the focus is on the specific modalities that must be included in the rehabilitation toolbox, the evidence for their effectiveness, and the problems and complications involved in getting and using them.

4.1   Descriptions of Treatment Modalities

Our prescriptions for treatment for the schizophrenia spectrum begin with rehabilitation counseling, the modality most central to psychiatric rehabilitation and recovery. After that, in keeping with the biosystems paradigm, the discussion is organized according to the level of biosystemic functioning addressed by the respective modalities, from neurophysiological to cognitive to behavioral skills to the social environment.

4.1.1   Rehabilitation Counseling and Related Modalities

Rehabilitation counseling is the core of psychiatric rehabilitation, generating the treatment targets, rehabilitation objectives, and recovery goals that drive the entire process. In that sense, it is inseparable from the treatment planning process itself (discussed in section 3.2). Primarily associated with the work of William Anthony and his colleagues, rehabilitation counseling represents a fusion of key concepts and principles from the psychology of physical rehabilitation and traditional client-centered psychotherapy. Its initial purpose is to recruit the client to the rehabilitation agenda, and to identify and commit to recovery goals. After that, the purpose is to identify personal assets, barriers, problems, and solutions that guide and inform the rehabilitation and recovery process (discussed in Section 3.2).

The primary aim in rehabilitation counseling is to help the client identify and commit to recovery goals

Rehabilitation counseling typically involves a periodic meeting between the person in recovery and at least one other member of the treatment and rehabilitation team. Both directive and nondirective psychotherapy techniques are employed to identify the problems that require treatment and rehabilitation, the person's desires and concerns, and resources to be applied. The initial objective is to reach consensus about the person's needs and what the team can do about them. A subsequent objective is to construct an individualized treatment and rehabilitation plan that integrates the team's goals and objectives with specific interventions and other services, bearing in mind that the person in recovery and/or substitute decision makers are key members of the team (see also Section 3.2). All the pharmacological and psychosocial modalities to be employed in the treatment and rehabilitation of the person in recovery are included on this plan, and it thus takes on a key role in consolidating each team member's understanding of the purpose and importance of each modality and service. This is seen as crucial to maximally engaging the person in recovery in his or her rehabilitation and ensuring high fidelity implementation of the treatment plan. As the treatment plan is implemented, the focus of counseling turns to appraisal and evaluation of progress, with the ongoing objective of reinforcing the person's experience of success and self-efficacy. Counseling continues until the treatment plan goals have been met and recovery is well underway.

There have been no separate controlled trials of rehabilitation counseling. It is considered a necessary component of psychiatric rehabilitation whose efficacy is reflected in the overall outcome of psychiatric rehabilitation. However, critical components of the counseling process have been studied, and newer modalities have been developed to address those components. The most basic component is simply providing information about the nature of the disorder and its treatment. This may seem a platitude, but such information is often surprisingly inaccessible to patients and their families, especially in medical model settings. Access to such information reduces distress and enhances engagement in treatment and rehabilitation. Empirical validation of the benefits of providing basic information began to appear in the 1990s and today psychoeducation is considered an essential part of psychiatric rehabilitation. Education of families is also demonstrably beneficial. Both dyadic and single-family psychoeducation formats are used, especially in early intervention/first episode programs. *Multi-family groups* also have demonstrated effectiveness,and have the added advantage of fostering social support networks. A complete toolkit for developing family psychoeducation programs can be obtained free of cost from SAMSHA (http://store.samhsa.gov/product/Family-Psychoeducation-Evidence-Based-Practices-EBP-KIT/SMA09-4423).

Motivational interviewing (MI; Miller & Rollnick, 2002) gives additional structure to the rehabilitation counseling process. MI is designed for use with people who are not initially enthusiastic or even voluntary therapy participants, originally people with substance abuse problems who have been coerced into treatment by family or the legal system. People with schizophrenia spectrum disorders are often in comparable circumstances. The original MI application for substance abuse works well with people who have schizophrenia spectrum disorders (e.g., Kelly, Daley, & Douaihy, 2012), and it also serves the broader purpose of fostering the person's engagement in rehabilitation and commit-

Although initially developed for substance abusing patients, motivational interviewing has been shown to be highly effective in the treatment of people with schizophrenia spectrum disorders

ment to recovery, independent of substance abuse issues (e.g., Bechdolf et al., 2012).

Acceptance and Commitment Therapy (ACT), a dialectical form of cognitive behavioral therapy, has purposes complementary to those of rehabilitation counseling (Bacon, Farhall, & Fossey, 2014), although so far its application has focused on reducing the distress caused by psychosis. More research using this modality for the schizophrenia spectrum is indicated, although initial evidence suggests that it reduces relapse and rehospitalization (Bach, Hayes, & Gallop, 2012).

4.1.2   Collaborative Psychopharmacotherapy

The biosystemic paradigm recognizes the potential importance of intervention at the neurophysiological level of functioning, as well as psychological and social levels. Analyses comparing the overall contributions of medication and psychosocial modalities have repeatedly shown that a combination is more effective than medication alone (Guo et al., 2010; Hogarty & Ulrich, 1998; Menditto et al., 1996; Mojtabai et al., 1998). It is also clear that pharmacological and psychosocial treatments interact. For example, some medications impair cognitive functions that are critical to recovery. This requires that the practitioners prescribing medication collaborate with the patient, the family, and the rest of the treatment team, working together to find a balance of controlling symptoms vs. avoiding cognitive impairment and other side effects, to minimize the barriers to reaching recovery goals.

The combination of medication and psychosocial treatment is almost always more effective than medication alone

This collaborative imperative was recognized in an early SAMSHA toolkit entitled "Collaborative Psychopharmacology," containing educational and program development materials to stimulate interdisciplinary collaboration. The original toolkit was removed from the SAMHSA website and replaced by "MedTEAM," which sustains the collaborative perspective. MedTEAM provides materials for comprehensively developing and evaluating collaborative psychopharmacotherapy in real world settings. The entire kit can be obtained free of charge from SAMSHA (http://store.samhsa.gov/product/MedTEAM-Medication-Treatment-Evaluation-and-Management-Evidence-Based-Practices-EBP-KIT/SMA10-4549). The kit includes an extensive reference list to support the practices it recommends, although there has been very little controlled research on the effectiveness of such kits for influencing practice and none on this particular kit.

Pharmacotherapy for the schizophrenia spectrum is employed for distinct but overlapping purposes, with different goals for short-term and long-term outcomes (see Section 1.4). The short-term purpose is stabilization of an acute psychotic episode. The longer-term purposes are to (1) prevent or postpone recurrence of psychotic episodes and (2) suppress psychotic symptoms residual to the acute episode. Individual responses to medications are highly variable and not highly predictable. Therefore, reliable ongoing assessment of medication effects on specific and quantified symptoms (see Section 3.1.1), or other behavioral treatment targets, as part of an integrated treatment, rehabilitation, and recovery plan, is an absolutely necessary feature of psychopharmacological treatment of schizophrenia spectrum disorders.

4.1.3   Neurocognitive Therapy

Impairments in *neurocognition* are common, if not universal, in schizophrenia spectrum disorders (see Section 2.8). As this realization spread across the research community, the idea of directly targeting and treating those impairments has gained importance, especially as psychopharmacotherapy proved ineffective (see Section 4.2). Today it is a robust area of treatment development, though somewhat complicated by inconsistency in terminology and principles. There is no universal agreement about which cognitive processes are *neurocognitive* (in some sense they all are), and the treatment targets range from the most elemental, e.g., perception, attention, and memory, to complex, high-level cognition, e.g., person perception, attribution, and other aspects of social cognition. There has been persistent skepticism about whether neurocognitive impairments in the schizophrenia spectrum can be changed at all, a belief reinforced (in the views of some) by the new concept of neurodevelopmental disorder, and so debate has persisted about whether the term *remediation* should ever be used to describe this approach. Nevertheless, *cognitive remediation* is often used, though it remains unclear what treatment effects truly remediate impairments, as opposed to enhancing compensatory abilities. Similarly, *training* is sometimes used to describe the treatment procedures, but without clear evidence that there are learning processes involved. One related approach makes no assumption about therapeutic change at all, but is focused instead on environmental modifications to compensate for cognitive deficits (Velligan et al., 2015).

For the purposes of this discussion, *neurocognitive therapy* is the best term for this area of psychiatric rehabilitation, keeping in mind that *neurocognitive* covers a broad range of cognitive processes. The key feature is that the treatment targets are impaired *processes*, as opposed to maladaptive *content* (e.g., false beliefs, low self-esteem).

Development of neurocognitive therapy began with adaptation of methods from experimental psychopathology. For example, *dichotic listening procedures* used to demonstrate auditory selective attention deficits have also been adapted to enable patients to practice attending to relevant stimuli and ignoring irrelevant stimuli. This technique helps patients cope with the distracting effects of auditory hallucinations, but even patients who do not experience hallucinations benefit from improved selective attention. A related approach uses computers to administer tasks based on neuropsychological tests and exercises developed for remediation of cognitive deficits in other disorders, e.g., learning disabilities. Such tasks and exercises have been incorporated in computerized packages with special education techniques, e.g., *Neuropsychological Educational Approach to Rehabilitation* (NEAR; e.g., Medalia, Revheim, & Casey, 2001). A core feature of the NEAR model is attention to intrinsic motivation and task engagement, through contextualizing tasks in real-world situations, multisensory stimulation, and personalization of and control over the learning activity. NEAR has demonstrated effectiveness in improving neurocognitive functioning, coping with symptoms, and making positive social impressions, in outpatient and chronic inpatient settings, and patients experience it as an enjoyable activity. Treatment effects of related computerized neurocognitive therapy modalities have also proven robust (e.g., Harvey &

Bowie, 2012), and the direct effects on cognition appear to enhance progress in other domains of rehabilitation and recovery (McGurk, Twamley, Sitzer, McHugo, & Mueser, 2007).

A general problem in psychiatric rehabilitation is that many interventions are inaccessible to patients with severe impairment in attention. These patients cannot attend to any material presented to them for a sufficient length of time. Any skill training may be compromised, and neurocognitive therapy targeting higher-level cognition in these patients may lead to clinical deterioration. For this group, improvements have been reported using the behavioral technique of shaping. *Shaping* is a method to achieve operant conditioning, and (duration of) attentive behavior frequently is a specifically targeted response. The primary technique involved is differential reinforcement of successive approximations to the final target behavior. For example, rather than waiting for the complete behavior (e.g., a 30-minute attention span) to occur before offering reinforcement, reinforcement is· provided for successive approximations or small steps toward the final behavior. When the initial step toward a behavior (e.g., three minutes of continuous attention) has been reinforced and occurs fairly regularly, the criterion for reinforcement is raised to a more challenging level (e.g., four minutes of continuous attention), and so on. Attention shaping leads to greater learning in group skill training (Silverstein et al., 2008), and improved attention generalizes to groups other than those in which shaping is included (Silverstein, et al., 2014).

> Shaping can be useful when working with clients who have problems with attention

A technique similar to shaping is *errorless learning* (Kern et al., 2005). Errorless learning involves initial training on tasks where there is a high expectation of success and proceeding through a graded series of tasks that become increasingly more complex. The goal of this procedure is to minimize the commission of errors while at the same time achieving performance mastery. Once a criterion level of performance is achieved, tasks at the next level of complexity are introduced. Errorless learning has demonstrated effectiveness in the treatment of developmentally disabled and neurologically impaired individuals. In the schizophrenia spectrum it produces improvement on neuropsychological tests of attention, memory, and executive cognition. The benefits extend to general progress in neurocognitive recovery, vocational functioning, and problem solving abilities.

Cognitive interventions are most effective when embedded within activities and settings that are meaningful to the person receiving them. S*upported cognition* interventions integrate neuropsychological and behavioral approaches *in vivo* (e.g., Feeney & Ylvisaker, 2003). Neurocognitive therapy provided concurrently with vocational rehabilitation produces improved work attendance and performance (Fiszdon & Bell, 2004), compared to vocational rehabilitation alone. Neurocognitive therapy also enhances the outcome of supported employment (McGurk, Mueser et al., 2007).

4.1.4   Contingency Management

Contingency management is a genre of techniques that evolved from learning and social learning theories in the 1960s. They are especially important in psychiatric residential and nonacute inpatient settings. As community-based programs for people with schizophrenia have proliferated, relevance of contingency management to such programs has generalized. Nevertheless, contingency management is one of the most underutilized technologies in adult mental health services. In settings where contingency management is most needed, where people with especially severe cognitive impairments and high risk behaviors are served, implementation is often complicated or prevented by incompatibilities with traditional institutional administrative practices, professional and guild interests, and related factors (further discussed in Section 4.5).

The earliest applications of contingency management for schizophrenia spectrum disorders, in the form of token economies in psychiatric hospitals, provided strong empirical evidence of effectiveness in promoting adaptive behavior (Ayllon & Azrin, 1968; Paul & Lentz, 1977). In addition to general effects on maladaptive and adaptive behavior, when combined with other social-learning modalities, contingency management has been shown to be effective with two of the most troublesome and drug-resistant problems encountered in inpatient settings, aggression (Beck, Menditto, Baldwin, Angelone, & Maddox, 1991) and polydipsia (Baldwin, Beck, Menditto, Arms, & Cormier, 1992).

As psychiatric rehabilitation has evolved, the role of contingency management in enhancing engagement in rehabilitation activities has become increasingly important. In community settings, contingency management includes identification of target behaviors relevant to recovery goals and a complete functional analysis of the recovering person's circumstances and social environment (especially the family) for natural incentives and disincentives critical to engagement and ultimately to recovery. Identification and management of such natural contingencies is often one of the unique contributions made by the psychologist member of the interdisciplinary treatment team.

Especially in the earlier stages of recovery, some form of contingency management is often necessary to overcome the disruptive effect of psychosis on the person's adaptation and motivation systems. In today's neurodevelopmental perspective, we understand this need in terms of stimulus immediacy, a generalized consequence of neurocognitive impairment (discussed in Section 2.8). As in normal development, stimulus immediacy and need for therapeutic compensation dissipate as recovery proceeds.

4.1.5 Individual Psychotherapy

Cognitive Behavior Therapy (CBT)

There is no fine line between neurocognition and higher levels of cognition, but as the targets of treatment occupy higher levels, and as concerns shift from process integrity to the *content* of cognition (beliefs, attributions, attitudes, etc.), treatment selection segues from neurocognitive therapy to *cognitive behavior therapy* (CBT) and related modalities. These modalities are usually provided in an individual psychotherapy format, but treatment objectives and techniques overlap with various group modalities and also with rehabilitation counseling. This gives the treatment team some flexibility in strategizing how local resources can be brought to bear on recovery goals. For example, the roles of rehabilitation counselor, neurocognitive therapist, cognitive behavior therapist, and social skills trainer could be filled by one team member or several, depending on skill sets, relative costs, the local regulatory environment, etc.

CBT is a type of psychotherapy, based on principles of conditioning, learning, and cognition. CBT as applied to the schizophrenia spectrum has come to be known as CBTp (p for psychosis). The problems for which CBTp provides potential solutions include hallucinations, delusions, demoralization and hopelessness, anhedonia, poor interpersonal skills, poor judgment, poor performance of daily routines and demands, and emotional dysregulation. All CBT works best with patients who are willing to actively participate in the treatment.

Meta-analyses of CBTp have repeatedly confirmed significant effect sizes, compared to treatment as usual or supportive therapy, across representatively diverse subgroups of people with schizophrenia spectrum disorders. Effect sizes vary from *medium* to *large* depending on the meta-analytic procedures, targets of treatment, therapist training, and other contextual factors (e.g., Jauhar et al., 2014; Newton-Howes & Wood, 2013). Most attention has been focused on psychotic symptoms as the treatment targets, but as the recovery movement has revealed, people with schizophrenia spectrum disorders have other concerns that can serve as treatment targets, e.g., having friends and intimate relationships, finding self-acceptance and self-worth, coping with stress, having a more comfortable, orderly life, understanding their emotions better, resolving interpersonal conflicts. Effects of CBTp on psychotic symptoms may not be the most important ones, for many people.

Effect sizes for CBTp vary from medium to large

CBTp is still evolving. The role of neglect, abuse, and trauma in the schizophrenia spectrum has stimulated incorporation of dialectical and mindfulness-oriented techniques originally developed for emotion dysregulation and post-traumatic stress disorder. Meta-analysis of 13 outcome studies indicates benefits (Khoury, Lecomte, Gaudiano, & Paquin, 2013), but the role of improved emotional regulation in the treatment effect remains unclear. Another evolutionary direction focuses on the role of *self-schemata* and *autobiographical narrative* in recovery. An evidence-based, manual-driven therapy emphasizing reconstruction of personal history and sense of self was developed by Gerard Hogarty in the 1990s (Hogarty et al., 1997) outside of mainstream CBT research. Today this direction is evident in so-called *metacognitive* approaches (e.g., Lysaker, et al., 2015), and these often focus specifically on reducing internalized stigma. Emotional regulation and self-schemata are promising areas of study for the near future, as research continues to identify the critical active ingredients in CBT (and other types of therapy) for addressing specific problems in specific contexts.

In addition to problems uniquely associated with psychotic disorders, various forms of CBT are effective for addressing generalized anxiety, panic, social anxiety, depression, and obsessive-compulsive symptoms. These problems often occur in the schizophrenia spectrum, and there is no reason to believe that the relevant CBT interventions are any less effective for people with schizophrenia spectrum disorders. In fact, CBT treatment for negative symptoms can be indistinguishable from CBT treatment for depression. In medical model settings or other settings insensitive to recovery principles, these problems are often overlooked as separate targets for treatment, because they are unreflectively attributed to "the schizophrenia."

Psychoanalysis and Psychoanalytic Therapies

In the wake of negative findings in early studies in the 1960s and the purge of psychoanalysis in the neo-Kraepelinian era (discussed in Section 1.1.2) psychodynamic therapies for schizophrenia came under attack as being not helpful and possibly harmful. However, the early studies were methodologically flawed, and later studies with more careful attention to therapist training, stability of the patient, and the purposes of therapy were more positive. Most recently psychodynamic therapy has shown effectiveness in facilitating recovery in people experiencing a first episode of psychosis (Harder, Koester, Valbak, & Rosenbaum, 2014).

> **Psychodynamic approaches may be helpful as clients struggle to understand the meaning of illness**

The psychodynamic perspective is not solely a treatment approach, but also a set of principles for understanding behavior that overlap with other approaches. For example, discussion of dreams can be useful in cognitive behavioral therapy, as metaphors for exploring beliefs and other cognitive schemata (Rosner, Lyddon, & Freeman, 2004). Discussion of hallucinations as metaphorical experiences can be a fruitful technique for patients who are able to engage in it (Silverstein, 2007). The recovery movement with its emphasis on subjective well-being provides another reason to re-evaluate the possible contribution of psychodynamic principles and techniques to psychiatric rehabilitation (Spaulding & Nolting, 2006; Lysaker, Glynn, Wilkniss, & Silverstein, 2010). Like CBT, psychodynamic approaches are evolving, and sometimes converging with other approaches.

4.1.6   Social Skills Training

Social skills training is familiar to many mental health professionals, having been widely applied to a variety of recipient populations, for the purpose of improving interpersonal functioning. There are highly developed and manualized versions designed specifically for the schizophrenia spectrum (e.g., Bellack, Mueser, Gingerich, & Agresta, 2004). Original research studies and meta-analyses have been consistent in showing that formal social skills training improves personal and social functioning, reduces hospital recidivism, and moderates symptoms in people who live with schizophrenia. Today group-format social skills training specialized for the schizophrenia spectrum is universally accepted as an essential EBP in the psychiatric rehabilitation toolbox. In the 1990s packaged materials for providing social skills training were developed, tested, and disseminated by the UCLA Clinical Research Center for Schizophrenia and Psychiatric Rehabilitation. The UCLA Social and Independent Living Skills modules are widely used in the United States and have been translated into 23 languages. They form the backbone of many inpatient and outpatient rehabilitation programs. The descendants of these materials, comparable to the SAMSHA toolkits in comprehensively supporting provision of the modality, are commercially available today from Psychiatric Rehabilitation Consultants (http://www.psychrehab.com; see Resources section).

> **Social skills training is most effective in a group setting that is structured and highly interactive**

Social skills training of the type known to be effective for people who live with schizophrenia is an energetic, highly structured, highly interactive group modality. It involves almost continuous use of role playing exercises, with all group members serving as observers, feedback providers (e.g., regarding specific behaviors such as level of eye contact, body posture, tone and volume of voice, choice of words, etc.), and assistants when not actually role-playing. It is necessary for the therapist to engage the people participating in training and facilitate their active participation throughout treatment. Unfortunately, "social skills groups" in mental health settings are often unstructured and ineffective. The availability of therapist training materials and related resources make it possible for most mental health settings to be able to provide high quality services, but only if the training is actually done and high fidelity to training precepts is assured by quality assurance mechanisms. Fidelity to the treatment manual is significantly related to patient outcomes (Wallace, Liberman, MacKain, Blackwell, & Eckman, 1992).

Social skills training is increasingly integrated with neurocognitive therapy techniques (see Section 4.1.3). In addition to the influence of neuropsychology and experimental psychopathology, work in this area was stimulated by the work of Donald Meichenbaum, a prominent figure in the development of modern cognitive-behavioral therapy, who showed that the familiar technique of self-guiding self-talk produces improvements on various cognitive measures in people with schizophrenia.

One example of a combined neurocognitive-social skills modality is *Integrated Psychological Therapy* (IPT; Roder, Müller, Brenner, Spaulding, 2011). This intervention targets skills in a hierarchical fashion, beginning with executive functioning, and moving through social perception, verbal communication, basic social skills, and interpersonal problem solving segments. Skills are targeted through group practice and problem solving using a series of exercises that increase in complexity over time. The first randomized controlled trial demonstrating unique benefits of neurocognitive therapy (Spaulding, Fleming et al., 1999; Spaulding, Reed, Sullivan, Richardson, & Weiler, 1999) used the cognitive components of IPT as the experimental treatment condition. Gerard Hogarty and his colleagues developed a similar modality, *cognitive enhancement therapy (CET* Hogarty, Flesher et al., 2004). CET is theoretically derived from developmental models of schizophrenia, and therefore conceptualizes many of the deficits patients have in terms of their failures to develop age appropriate cognitive and social cognitive skills. Both IPT and CET are commercially produced as manuals with related materials, ready for implementation by psychologists sufficiently familiar with cognitive assessment of schizophrenia spectrum disorders and basic group-format skill training. They are extremely useful for introducing both cognitive and social skill capabilities into a psychiatric rehabilitation array.

Since development of CET, the distinction between neurocognition and social cognition (see Section 2.8) has led to modalities more focused on the latter, stimulated by findings that measures of social cognition (e.g., affect recognition, person perception, theory of mind) tend to be more strongly correlated to in vivo functioning than neuropsychological and related measures of more molecular cognitive processes. An example is *Social Cognition and Interaction Training* (SCIT; Roberts et al., 2014). Principles of metacognitive therapy are also applicable (Ottavi et al., 2014). The near future will probably see more integrated combinations of neurocognitive, social cognitive, and social skills techniques, packaged for efficient implementation in psychiatric rehabilitation settings.

4.1.7   Problem Solving Skills Training

A widely used social skills training format, developed and disseminated by the UCLA Center for Research On Treatment and Rehabilitation of Psychosis, uses *interpersonal problem-solving*, a classic CBT technique (D'Zurilla & Goldfried, 1971). The approach uses a heuristic model of problem-solving. The model has five stages: detection and identification of the problem, generation of possible solution scenarios, selection of a solution, implementation of the solution, and evaluation of the results. Participants learn this model, and then apply it to problems they have identified in their own lives. The cognitive and behavioral skills relevant to each stage are specifically rehearsed. It is generally accepted that cognitive behavioral problem solving is a key component of social skills training. Therefore, in addition to forming the content of separate problem-solving groups, problem-solving activities, using the five steps outlined above, are incorporated into all of the UCLA skills training packages. Problem-solving techniques continue to be incorporated and studied in comprehensive psychiatric rehabilitation programs (Granholm, Holden, Link, & McQuaid, 2014). As neurocognitive, social cognitive, and problem-solving techniques are increasingly combined in integrated and packaged modalities, the distinctions between them become less meaningful.

4.1.8   Illness/Wellness Management Skills Training

Gaining the ability to manage one's own psychiatric illness is central to the rehabilitation and recovery perspective. In the psychiatric rehabilitation literature, skill training in illness/wellness management has gradually differentiated itself from related social and living skills approaches, reflecting a growing recognition that specialized skills are needed to self-manage psychiatric disorders, comparable to skills needed to self-manage severe and persistent physical conditions such as diabetes. Participants learn about the episodic and persistent symptoms of their illness, the relationship between these symptoms and functional impairments, pharmacological and other techniques (e.g., relaxation and stress management) for controlling the symptoms, drug side effects, identification of *warning signs* of an impending relapse, and various other aspects of their disorder and its management. Behavioral skills indirectly relevant to disorder management are included, for example, the assertive skills necessary for dealing with the doctor and the doctor's receptionist in getting an appointment for a medication review. The skill training also usually includes some form of *relapse prevention* specialized for relapse of acute psychosis (Klingberg et al., 2010). This usually involves construction of a document that identifies warning signs (indicators of possibly impending psychosis) and specific plans and directions for protective actions to be taken. Additionally, relapse prevention plans may specify assistance desired during times of increased symptoms or crises from key supports in the person's life such as family members or friends.

Throughout the 1990s controlled trials confirmed the effectiveness of various versions of illness/wellness management skill training, and several developer groups have packaged materials for testing and dissemination. The US Substance Abuse and Mental Health Services Administration (SAMHSA) has produced a toolkit, "Illness Management and Recovery," which includes materials for all participants in the illness/wellness management process, including the person in recovery, medication prescriber, other service providers, family, and friends. It can be obtained free of charge from SAMSHA (http://store.samhsa.gov/product/Illness-Management-and-Recovery-Evidence-Based-Practices-EBP-KIT/SMA09-4463). Medication management and symptom management modules are included in the skill training materials available from Psychiatric Rehabilitation Consultants (http://www.psychrehab.com). Development of illness/wellness management modalities continues today, including specialization for specific subgroups (e.g., older people) and integration with related rehabilitation modalities (e.g., Mueser et al., 2010).

Several toolkits have been developed for skill training in illness/wellness management

A similar modality is *wellness and recovery action plan* (WRAP; Copeland, 1997). WRAP is closely associated with the consumerist recovery movement and disseminated mostly through channels outside the professional and scientific community. WRAP groups, led by non-professionals with personal experience with schizophrenia spectrum disorders and with training in the WRAP modality, produce reductions in symptom severity and increased hopefulness and quality of life, compared to *treatment as usual* (Cook et al., 2012). The non-professional nature of WRAP and the social support network it fosters are important features of this approach. Although it is not yet clear that WRAP can supplant the evidence-based modalities designed to be led by mental health practitioners, they are not incompatible. In some settings the didactic parts of WRAP may segue into an ongoing social support network, which would be a distinct benefit of its consumer-orientation.

4.1.9 Independent Living Skills Training

People who live with schizophrenia spectrum disorders often lose or fail to develop skills associated with routine daily living, such as basic personal healthcare, grooming and hygiene, keeping a daily schedule, housekeeping, cooking, management of personal funds, and using public resources (transportation, libraries, etc.). Acquisition of these skills contributes significantly to the ability to live safely and comfortably as members of the community. Of all skill domains, this one is relevant to the broadest range of neurodevelopmental disorders and disabilities. As a result, independent living skill programs have become ubiquitous in human service agencies, including developmental and mental health services. There is no reason to believe that people with schizophrenia spectrum disorders as a group have different living skill needs than groups with other disabilities, although different groups or individuals may need different kinds of support or assistance for successful skill acquisition. This needs to be taken into consideration when independent living skills training is included on the treatment plan.

People who participate in independent living skills training receive didactic instruction and in vivo coaching to establish the knowledge base and performance ability necessary to use specific skills. Empirical verification of the effectiveness of independent living skill training, in terms of increases in the skills taught, is provided by separate controlled trials (e.g., Moriana, Alarcón, & Herruzo, 2006), but is more commonly incorporated in assessments of more comprehensive rehabilitation programs that include or emphasize living skill training (e.g., Liberman, Glynn, Blair, Ross, & Marder, 2002). One of the UCLA Social and Independent Living Skills modules, Community Re-entry, addresses skills in this domain, and is available from Psychiatric Rehabilitation Consultants (http://www.psychrehab.com).

4.1.10 Specialized Integrated Treatment for Co-Occurring Substance Abuse

Co-occurring substance abuse is a widely recognized problem in the schizophrenia spectrum and is a cause of relapse and a barrier to rehabilitation and recovery. Conventional substance abuse approaches, such as 12-step programs, are effective for some people and should be included in a service array. However, many people with schizophrenia spectrum disorders do not benefit from conventional substance abuse approaches and require specialized programs specifically designed to address substance abuse within the context of psychiatric rehabilitation (e.g., Kavanagh, McGrath, Saunders, Dore, & Clark, 2002). Such approaches tend to lack the quasi-religious, confrontational, and moralistic features of 12-step programs, and employ a more social learning-based approach emphasizing development of self-regulation skills.

The Substance Abuse and Mental Health Services Administration (SAMHSA) has produced a package for public dissemination that falls under this category, co-occurring disorders: Integrated Dual Disorders Treatment (http://store.samhsa.gov/product/Integrated-Treatment-for-Co-Occurring-Disorders-Evidence-Based-Practices-EBP-KIT/SMA08-4367).   Recently SAMSHA has been criticized for obscuring the difference between schizophrenia spectrum disorders and less disabling conditions, e.g., anxiety, depression, and personality disorder, as they co-occur with substance abuse. Without specific outcome studies, the effectiveness of this SAMSHA toolkit is unclear. The UCLA group also developed an effective form of integrated dual disorder treatment, the Substance Abuse Management Module (Shaner, Eckman, Roberts, & Fuller, 2003), that recognizes the features of the schizophrenia spectrum co-occurring with substance abuse. Its descendant is available from Psychiatric Rehabilitation Consultants (http://www.psychrehab.com).

4.1.11 Supported Employment and Occupational Skills Training

Until recently, most people with schizophrenia who expressed an interest in working were placed in sheltered workshops or other settings where the jobs were reserved for people with a mental illness. This is known as the *train-place model*, because the idea was that vocational rehabilitation would eventually lead to placement in a real-world job. Train-place programs use sheltered workshops and work enclaves, which typically pay below minimum wage and lack community integration. Train-place models have been minimally effective with schizophrenia spectrum clients, with at most 20% achieving competitive employment. In the wake of psychiatric rehabilitation and the recovery movement, efforts are now made to place people in real world community job settings that reflect their interests and to provide them with supports necessary to succeed. This practice, based on a *place-train model*, is known as *supported employment* (SE). Supported *education* is a variant designed for people in the occupational role of "student." *Individual placement and support* (IPS) is a standardized version now used in a preponderance of the research.

SE fidelity criteria are radically different from those of traditional vocational rehabilitation:

- Anyone wanting to work is eligible.
- SE includes comprehensive assessment and services for all aspects of the disability, including psychiatric treatment and rehabilitation.
- SE includes *benefits counseling* (professional evaluation of the impact of working on the person's existing or potential disability pensions and related benefits).
- The initial focus is on getting competitive employment according to client preferences and recovery goals.
- Individualized support for keeping the chosen job is unlimited.

In supported employment programs employment specialists or *job coaches* are members of clients' treatment teams, to integrate vocational services with comprehensive psychiatric rehabilitation. The employment specialist provides the full range of vocational services, including identifying vocational interests and skills, job finding, and job support. Most services are delivered in clients' natural settings rather than mental health or rehabilitation facilities.

Job coaches are critical members of supported employment teams

Controlled studies have demonstrated superiority of SE programs over traditional work programs (e.g., Mueser et al., 2004). A toolkit for supported employment can be obtained at no cost from SAMSHA (http://store.samhsa. gov/product/Supported-Employment-Evidence-Based-Practices-EBP-KIT/ SMA08-4365).

In addition to SE, many people with a schizophrenia spectrum disorder need help with *general occupational skills*, skills that are important for most any work-related activity, e.g., punctuality, proper workplace grooming, staying on task, following instructions, managing relationships with coworkers and supervisors. These are separate from *vocational* skills, which are more specific to particular kinds of work. Providing such skill training outside one's place of employment is not necessarily reversion to a train-place model, nor incompatible with SE. Research generally supports the effectiveness of occupational skill training for increasing work-related performance (e.g., Wallace & Tauber, 2004) in people diagnosed with schizophrenia, although it is unclear whether it enhances the benefits of SE. Materials for the UCLA workplace skills training and leisure skills training (leisure skills are also important occupational skills) are available from Psychiatric Rehabilitation Consultants (http://www.psychrehab.com).

SE is widely accepted as an evidence-based practice. Nevertheless, the overall success rate for vocational rehabilitation in the schizophrenia spectrum remains low. SE does not clearly lead to normal, independent competitive employment. Its unlimited parameters make assessment of cost-effectiveness extremely difficult. High fidelity SE is difficult to achieve. Outcomes are best for people with less severe impairment in personal and social functioning.

Research on ways to enhance SE outcome, e.g., with neurocognitive therapy, social skills training, and occupational skills training, continues today. However, there is a limiting factor in the vocational domain of recovery that improved techniques may never surmount. Despite the valuation of work that appears in the recovery literature, many people with schizophrenia spectrum disorders choose to live on disability pensions instead (a reason why benefits counseling is a key component of SE). Adherence to the "work ethic" is not necessarily compatible with individual recovery choices. SE gives people a choice, and there is value in choice, independent of the vocational outcomes that are only important to people who want to work.

4.1.12 Family Therapy

A broad spectrum of family processes and therapies have long been of interest in schizophrenia spectrum research. In the 1950s, many believed that families, and parents in particular, played a causal role in the etiology of the disorder (discussed in Section 1.1.4). This view, which is distinct from recent findings that childhood trauma and neglect contribute to vulnerability, was never empirically supported and today is largely discredited. Nevertheless, family members often experience guilt and/or distress in this regard. Clinicians should always be vigilant for this possibility and intervene with corrective information when indicated. Psychoeducation (discussed in Section 4.1.1) often resolves much of the distress of having a family member with a schizophrenia disorder. However, many families experience additional conflicts, dilemmas, and challenges requiring a more intensive and individualized therapeutic approach.

Family psychoeducation, reduction of expressed emotion via teaching of communication skills, behavioral management, and social support became collectively known as *behavioral family therapy* (BFT). Outcome trials throughout the 1990s confirmed the effectiveness of BFT in reducing relapse and rehospitalization (Pilling et al., 2002). Today BFT is playing a critical role in early intervention programs. Development of BFT for the schizophrenia spectrum continues, with attention to achieving optimal adaptations for cultural subgroups (e.g., Weisman de Mamani, Weintraub, Gurak, & Maura, 2014).

Brief supportive interventions for families, ranging from one to eight sessions, have increased family members' sense of support from the treatment team, increased their knowledge about schizophrenia and its treatment and rehabilitation, improved their coping, reduced distress and self-blame, and increased satisfaction with services. These modalities include some psychoeducational features of family therapy (discussed in the previous section), but they have not been shown to reduce relapse or hospital recidivism. Nevertheless, the very large return for the small investment justifies advocacy for developing brief family support services in a service system.

4.1.13 Peer Support and Self-Help Groups

Peer support and self-help groups have been associated with the recovery movement throughout its recent history. *Peers* in this context are people in recovery from mental illness, usually self-identified. Their role in rehabilitation can range from being members of a self-organizing mutual support network to helpers assisting with performance of routine chores to WRAP group leaders (see section 4.1.8). Data has been accumulating for over a decade on the benefits of peer support of various kinds. Although the data are promising, there is also evidence that the benefits of peer support and self-help approaches are heavily moderated by the "fit" between the person in recovery and the rest of the group. The outcome data do not yet meet the criteria for evidence-based practice, but peer support programs of various kinds are proliferating (Duckworth & Halpern, 2014). Advocacy for peer support and related services may be justified by recovery principles and broader social values, but the scientific evidence base so far offers little guidance as to what services produce the most desirable benefits.

Self-help groups are an important component of the recovery movement

4.1.14 Acute Treatment, Crisis Intervention, and Related Services

The nature of schizophrenia spectrum disorders is such that people sometimes need a protected, secure environment for relatively brief periods of time. Historically psychiatric institutions masked this need because they were continuously protected and secure and insensitive to changes in patient's needs. Short-term psychiatric inpatient units in general hospitals arguably serve a comparable function today, but aside from preventing injury there is no reason to believe that acute hospitalization has any therapeutic benefit. There is no psychiatric treatment, pharmacological or psychosocial, that can only be provided in an acute inpatient setting (except in the sense that regulations may allow procedures such as restraint and seclusion to be done only in hospitals). Although acute hospitalization persists as a treatment option, it is not always under the control of the patient or the practitioner, and is often the consequence of legal interventions such as civil commitment. Unfortunately, the very high cost of hospitalization can make jail appear to be a cost-effective alternative, and this partly accounts for the very high proportion of people with schizophrenia spectrum disorders in jails and prisons. The practitioner must be prepared to deal with hospitalization, or more explicit forms of incarceration, not as a treatment but as an environmental event for which people with schizophrenia spectrum disorders are at high risk.

There are evidence-based alternatives to psychiatric hospitalization as a way to manage periods of heightened protection and security needs. Crises in schizophrenia may be driven by a host of factors other than psychotic relapse, and in such cases addressing those factors in a timely way may be more important than removing the person to a protected environment and administering drugs. As a result, alternative crisis services and 24-hour respite facilities are increasingly included in mental health systems. Often, these are incorporated in a comprehensive case management system. Controlled research on crisis hostels has not reached the level of evidence-based practice, but the existing research and the social value of consumer involvement identify crisis hostels and related alternatives to acute inpatient hospitalization as promising practices (Simpson & Moriarty, 2014). Practitioners should seek opportunities to advocate for such alternatives in the service systems in which they practice.

4.1.15   Specialized Models for Service Integration and Provision

The importance of coordination and integration of treatment and other services is arguably greater in psychiatric rehabilitation than many other areas of mental health, just because of the sheer number of services and practitioners involved. The heterogeneity of the population and the need for personalized rehabilitation and recovery plans add to the challenges. In addition, healthcare regulation standards and funding channels tend to incentivize provision of complex services to special populations through *programs*, organized packages of specific services. In response to these demands, specialized *organizational models* for psychiatric rehabilitation have evolved and have accumulated empirical validation for enhancing outcomes.

The *default mode* of organizational models is *case management*, a simple arrangement in which a specified professional or paraprofessional performs the role of case manager, identifying needed services, helping the patient make and keep appointments, and helping with routines of daily living. Conventional case management is a derivation of medical model social work, and is ineffective in a rehabilitation and recovery paradigm without extensive modifications. Most importantly, it does not involve data-based construction or strategic implementation of a personalized rehabilitation and recovery plan. All organizational models include some form of case management, but without further enhancements, case management and maintenance pharmacotherapy constitute *treatment as usual*, often the control condition in experimental trials of psychiatric rehabilitation modalities. Unfortunately, though this is barely distinguishable from *no* treatment as usual, it is the only service option available to the vast majority of people with schizophrenia spectrum disorders in the US.

The Psychosocial Clubhouse Model

Invented by former patients of state hospitals in New York, the *psychosocial clubhouse model* actually predates the deinstitutionalization era, but it can be a cost-effective organizational structure for modern psychiatric rehabilitation. The key features of the model are a social club-like organization, a community of participants with psychiatric disabilities as club members, the inclusion of club members in administrative roles, an emphasis on mutual peer support, and operation in a physical residential or occupational setting, or both. Exemplars include Fountain House (Fisher & Beard, 1962), Thresholds (Bond, Dincin, Setze & Witheridge, 1984), and the Fairweather Lodge (Fairweather, Sanders, Maynard & Cressler, 1969). Today, specific treatment and rehabilitation services are often provided through variations of the clubhouse model, including social, living, and occupational skill training in residential settings

Fountain House, Thresholds, and the Fairweather Lodge are historically important models for the clubhouse model of treatment

(e.g., residential rehabilitation programs) and day rehabilitation programs. Both residential and day rehabilitation clubhouse programs provide important sites for skill training, therapy, rehabilitation counseling, peer support groups, and other rehabilitation/ recovery services. The service array may or may not be comprehensive, and may or may not include treatment planning and case management. If not comprehensive, specific services are coordinated with other providers. Clubhouse models generally emphasize consumer involvement and peer support, and are in that sense especially consistent with the social values associated with rehabilitation and recovery.

Social Learning Programs

Social learning programs (SLPs) also have pre-deinstitutionalization origins in the token economy research of the 1960s (see also Section 4.1.4). SLPs are comprehensive, integrated networks of learning-based techniques and skills-training modalities delivered by specially trained staff within in a supportive, rehabilitation-oriented program. The overwhelming superiority of a SLP in helping people move from psychiatric institution to community (Paul & Lentz, 1977) was a landmark in the evolution of psychiatric rehabilitation. SLPs are especially well suited to high-security and/or high intensity treatment settings that serve people whose personal and social functioning is so impaired that being in a less secure or acceptable setting incurs unacceptable risks. Almost by definition, this disproportionately includes people deemed refractory to all pharmacological treatment (although the more technical meaning of refractory is actually refractory to first-generation antipsychotics; see Section 4.1.2). However, modified SLPs in less intensive settings, e.g., transitional units in institutions, community residential programs, produce comparably superior outcomes. In the post-deinstitutionalization era, this means helping people move to less restrictive and more independent settings, from wherever they start out. SLPs provide an organizational model equally suitable for services at multiple levels of care, providing continuity as people undertake the earliest and most difficult stages of their recovery journey. Without such resources in high intensity restrictive settings, for many the journey cannot begin.

Consistent with the Paul & Lentz (1977) prototype, modern comprehensive SLPs include a number of key factors critical to their success:

- Rehabilitation philosophy and values
- Learning-based techniques
- Direct skills training
- Formal contingency management
- Functional and behavioral assessment systems
- Staff training and supervision specific to SLP procedures
- The program is part of an integrated continuum of care from high intensity settings to independent living

Assertive Community Treatment

Assertive community treatment (ACT) was arguably the first new organizational model to emerge after deinstitutionalization. In its original form, it was characterized as *a hospital without walls* because it was designed to project a conventional medical model of institutional care into community settings. The key feature was a community-based version of institutional psychiatric treatment teams, a psychiatrist, a social worker, nurse, and direct care staff, operating from a problem-oriented treatment plan, but uninformed by modern psychiatric rehabilitation. Another key feature was exclusive responsibility for all care by the treatment team. This made sense in the deinstitutionalization era, when communities had no resources or infrastructure for serving people with disabling schizophrenia spectrum disorders. However, as the rehabilitation and recovery era progressed, this exclusivity became a barrier to accessing other community services and a hobbling limitation of the model. Not surprisingly, the original ACT model proved effective at maintaining people in the community, forestalling relapses and returns to the institution, but not at improving personal and social functioning as demanded by modern recovery principles.

SAMHSA has developed a free toolkit for developing assertive community treatment programs

At least one version of ACT has been commercially packaged as a proprietary product (Allness & Knoedler, 2003). A SAMHSA toolkit for developing ACT in a service system is available from SAMSHA free of cost (http://store.samhsa.gov/product/Assertive-Community-Treatment-ACT-Evidence-Based-Practices-EBP-KIT/SMA08-4345). By following the manual and using the materials, which include quality assurance and program evaluation tools, treatment teams can credibly provide services according to a standard model.

There has been much research on the efficacy and cost-effectiveness of ACT programs, but the results are complex. Approximately 5–20% of patients with serious mental illness (at least half of whom are diagnosed with schizophrenia) do not function well in ACT, but the reasons for this are unclear. Although the effects of ACT on re-hospitalization are relatively robust, actual recovery depends on inclusion of psychiatric rehabilitation modalities. The outcome picture is further obscured by differences in subject populations across studies and differences in the surrounding mental health service system. Nevertheless, it is reasonably clear that the ACT organizational model must be amplified with recovery-oriented assessment and treatment planning and an array of psychiatric rehabilitation modalities to meet contemporary expectations for outcomes.

High Risk, First Episode, and Early Intervention Programs
With the publication of the first RCT of an integrated, multimodal treatment program for people with recent onset of a schizophrenia spectrum disorder (Kane et al., 2016), the probable importance of such programs in the near future increased dramatically. This cannot yet be considered a distinct evidence-based organizational model, but it almost certainly will be within a few years. The modalities typically included in such programs have outcomes already validated in other settings or contexts, e.g., illness/wellness management training, supported employment, neurocognitive therapy, CBTp, and social skills training. Considering the promise of these programs for reducing morbidity and disability, their dissemination could be one of the most important developments in mental health in the coming decade.

Organizational Models in the Full Service Array
Clubhouse models, ACT, residential SLPs, and early intervention programs are cost-effective service models for ranges of individuals within the schizophrenia spectrum. It may seem obvious that people with vastly different needs and levels of functioning might optimally benefit from different service arrays,

but it is an idea that does not always survive the mental health services planning process. System administrators tend to adopt a *one size fits all* attitude, naively choosing one favored model to meet all needs. For the schizophrenia spectrum, the practice of clinical psychology usually must include advocacy for service diversification and personalization, as well as for evidence-based practice.

A "one-size-fits-all" mentality pervades mental health administration

Generally, clubhouse models are most cost-effective for people who have realized a substantial degree of stability and are motivated for and invested in recovery. People whose disorder is less stable have a higher level of disability, and/or who are less able to sustain their engagement in rehabilitation and recovery, are expected to benefit more from ACT. There is a range of persons who, in the later stages of the process of recovery, require less service integration and support than clubhouse programs provide, and for them conventional case management is sufficient to coordinate needed services. At the other end of the continuum, a small but significant proportion of the population, at an earlier stage of recovery, does not do well in clubhouse programs or ACT. Also, some people cannot access clubhouse programs or ACT until later stages of recovery, for legal and public safety reasons. For these people, the organizational model of residential social learning-based rehabilitation provides the best alternative. It is important to note, in this regard, that social learning programs' key outcome is their effectiveness at helping people move to less intensive/restrictive circumstances, including clubhouse and ACT programs, conventional case management, and independent living. In fact, step-down SLPs in community residential settings can not only provide the critical first step out of the institution for people with the most severe disabilities, but also boost people to levels of functioning high enough to avert their need for ACT or residential clubhouse levels of care (Tarasenko, Sullivan, Ritchie, & Spaulding, 2013).

4.1.16 Supported Housing

Supported housing is neither a treatment modality nor a specific organizational model, but the fundamental importance of having a stable place to live has inspired a social movement focused on securing housing for people with psychiatric disabilities and then providing whatever support is necessary for keeping them there. In that sense, the supported housing movement is one more example of the *place-train approach* (see Section 4.1.11). Supported housing has also become a social policy and human rights issue in the post-deinstitutionalization era, increasingly associated with *Olmstead v. L.C.*, a US Supreme Court ruling affirming the rights of all people to live as much as possible in a normal community setting. This is a reaction to the congregation of deinstitutionalized people who live in squalor in "mental health ghettos," ramshackle hotels, and abusive group homes, because state mental health systems do not provide treatment, rehabilitation, or support sufficient for those people to live in more normal circumstances. In this sense, supported housing broadly includes psychiatric rehabilitation, because once physical housing is secured, people's recovery goals tend to include taking care of their home and themselves more independently.

Olmstead v. L.C. **was a Supreme Court ruling that affirmed the right of all people to live in as normal a community setting as possible**

If putting primacy on housing helps persons with schizophrenia spectrum disorders develop a stable home in the community, it would qualify as an evidence-based practice or policy, if not a treatment. On the other hand, an ambitious policy of independent housing is not likely to maintain long-term residential stability without consideration of such factors as substance abuse, an individual's social network, poverty, quality of housing, criminal activity in the neighborhood, and the amount and quality of ongoing, personalized treatment, support, and assistance from community-based mental health teams. There is much to be learned about how to meet the demands of *Olmstead*, including how to integrate the principles of supported housing with the other dimensions of rehabilitation and recovery.

4.2   Mechanisms of Action

Schizophrenia spectrum disorders are complex, and comprehensive treatment requires intervention at multiple levels, typically including pharmacological, cognitive, behavioral, family, the broader social environment, and even cultural. Mechanisms of change operate at all of these levels as well.

Consideration of treatment mechanisms must begin with the classical distinction between specific and nonspecific factors. There is no reason to expect that the familiar therapeutic characteristics of practitioners, i.e., empathetic, nonjudgmental, and authentic, have any less impact on patients with schizophrenia spectrum disorders than anyone else. When the patient's milieu includes a positive relationship and a therapeutic alliance with providers, outcome is better (Mojtabai et al., 1998; Saunders & Lueger, 2005).

A second consideration is the nature of causality in biosystems. While it is possible to compute correlations between elements in an etiological theory of the schizophrenia spectrum, the directions of influence between elements of any complex system are predominantly mutual and reciprocal. This means that the effects of "tweaking" any particular element with a treatment intervention will inevitably be distributed throughout the system. The outcome of treating systemic conditions like the schizophrenia spectrum is determined by the total number of "tweaks" that can be brought to bear across all levels of functioning, not a "magic bullet" aimed at a single origin (for further discussion of this principle, see Spaulding et al., 2003). Therefore, even when we identify a specific treatment-response relationship, the "downstream" consequences of the response may be as important as the more immediate effects. Our neurodevelopmental understanding of the schizophrenia spectrum compounds the implications of this principle. The most critical treatment effects may be downstream consequences of treatment that reset or restart critical developmental sequences.

At the neurophysiological level, blockade of the D2 dopamine receptor is clearly a critical link in the mechanism of the antipsychotic effect, but the reasons remain mysterious (discussed in Section 2.6). D2 blockade probably quells one or more dopaminergic systems made overactive, by stress, inflammation, or informational overload generated by "upstream" dysregulation, e.g., of the glutamate system. The partial D2 agonist aripiprazole may perform a dual function, suppressing subcortical dopamine hyperactivation while moderating or reversing cortical hypoactivation.

The corticostriatal probabilistic learning mechanism described in Section 2.6 can account for the effects of neurocognitive therapy on post-acute cognitive impairment. Although the probabilistic learning mechanism continues to attract attention as an etiological factor in the schizophrenia spectrum (Strauss, Whearty, Frost, & Carpenter, 2016), its role in acute psychosis and the effects of neurocognitive therapy have not been experimentally evaluated.

Neurocognitive therapy also appears to exert its effects through top down mechanisms, such as enhancing activation of the cognitive operations most appropriate for a given situation or task, whether or not it affects the operations themselves. Similarly, effectiveness is a function of the extent to which variables such as motivation, self-efficacy, and task engagement are addressed (Medalia & Brekke, 2010).

Ordinary social learning theory can account for much of the impact of cognitive behavioral therapy and skill training, although it does not explain the need for acquiring skills normally developed in childhood and adolescence. The neurodevelopmental perspective has much potential in this regard. At least some of the abilities acquired in therapy and skill training may be skills that were simply not acquired normally in development, and treatment provides a belated opportunity. However, it also appears that many abilities are lost in the prodrome and early course of the illness. Disruption of behavioral organization mechanisms, e.g., the corticostriatal probabilistic learning mechanism, may at least partially account for the loss, and recovery of that system may account for some therapy and skill training effects. For most patients, it is probably a combination of acquiring new skills and recovering lost ones.

Theories of CBT in general increasingly include concepts such as *the self*, and related coordination of cognitive activity. Abnormalities in the organization and experience of the self are prominent features of schizophrenia, presumably due to both neurodevelopmental failures and the impact of psychosis in adulthood. A convergence of CBT and neurocognitive principles toward targeting such abnormalities is already evident in metacognitive therapy approaches (see Section 4.1.5).

The coping and stress management skills acquired in CBT may have downstream effects on the hypothalamic-pituitary-adrenal (HPA) activation system. Persistent over-activation of this system leads initially to elevated levels of the activating hormone cortisol, as observed in people with acute psychosis. Cortisol is neurotoxic, and chronic elevations may have a long-term detrimental effect on various brain systems. In chronic schizophrenia spectrum disorders, cortisol levels are extremely low, partly because of suppression by antipsychotic drugs, but possibly also due to a long-term "burnout" of the HPA system. The levels may be so low that the normal diurnal cortisol cycle is obscured. Cortisol is an important factor in regulating diurnal brain activation, and persistently low cortisol levels may contribute to negative symptoms and cognitive impairments.

Stabilization of dysregulated behavioral avoidance mechanisms may be an important mechanism of both pharmacological and psychosocial treatment. Avoidance is a preferred coping strategy among many people with episodic psychosis, but they become less avoidant with rehabilitation (Böker

& Brenner, 1983). In animal models, suppression of a previously conditioned escape/avoidance response is the first detectable effect of antipsychotic drugs (Smith, Li, Becker, & Kapur, 2004).

4.2.1   Recovery-Oriented Perspectives

The recovery movement has stimulated much research on the experience of individuals that may contribute to our understanding of the mechanisms of recovery (Spaulding et al., 2016). Qualitative analyses of personal recovery narratives identify several themes: the importance of work and the social role of the worker, expectations and attitudes toward treatment, eliminating symptoms, gaining an understanding and a sense of control over the illness, restoring premorbid functioning, establishing and maintaining satisfying relationships. Work is viewed as a context to practice skills, a setting for providing social contacts, an avenue for generating a more functional sense of self and higher self-esteem, an activity that diminishes symptoms, generating purpose and meaning in one's life, and providing a source of money and material survival. In contrast, not working reinforces a sense of shame, helplessness, and lack of agency.

Converging with Hogarty's personal therapy and metacognitive ideas in therapy, autobiographical *recovery narratives* are critical in *self-transformation*, a process of creating a new understanding of who we are (Lysaker et al., 2015; Roe et al., 2014). Such narratives often revolve around a decisive change in the course of one's life. For many people with a schizophrenia spectrum disorder, adopting a recovery perspective is such a decisive change. The near future is likely to see intensive research on how people develop and use autobiographical narrative in self-transformation and recovery from schizophrenia spectrum disorders.

4.3   Efficacy and Effectiveness

Efficacy is demonstrated in controlled settings, while effectiveness is studied under real world conditions

Efficacy is what can be demonstrated under highly controlled conditions, e.g., in clinical laboratories or research clinics. *Effectiveness* is the impact of a practice on problems in the real world, under the conditions in which mental health services are generally provided. We expect that effective practices are derived or developed from efficacious procedures in research studies, and this is a central tenet of evidence-based practice (discussed in Section 1.1.7). However, the transition from a research procedure to a clinical practice is fraught with difficulty and complication, and is not a linear, systematic, or purely scientific process (Wykes & Spaulding, 2011).

Historically, efficacy and effectiveness were intertwined in schizophrenia spectrum research. Landmark studies, e.g., of the early token economies and social learning programs, were conducted in real world psychiatric institutions, with real world outcomes. As psychiatric rehabilitation diversified and modalities proliferated, the question of whether experimental treatments have impact in real world settings became more pointed. The most proximal effects of psychological treatment, e.g., higher scores on cognitive or social skill measures, do not necessarily produce better personal and social functioning. Also, the settings in which people with schizophrenia spectrum disorders are served have themselves diversified to include community residential facilities, day programs, special clinics, outreach programs, and others. Gradually, as specific rehabilitation modalities demonstrate effectiveness, the research is turning to efficacy studies in specific kinds of settings and for specific subpopulations, e.g., motivational interviewing with veterans (Sherman et al., 2009), integrated rehabilitation for older populations (Mueser et al., 2010), and CBTp in various settings (e.g., Lincoln et al., 2012).

The most reliable estimates of efficacy are the *effect sizes* generated by meta-analyses of controlled treatment trials. The most familiar effect size statistic, *Cohen's d*, describes the average difference between experimental and control conditions across studies. Values of *d* less than .3 are considered *small* effect sizes, larger than .8 are *large*, and in between are *medium*, although such categorizations are context-dependent and ultimately arbitrary. In psychiatric rehabilitation, effect sizes range from about .5 for antipsychotic medication effects on psychotic symptoms (Leucht, Arbter, Engel, Kissling, & Davis, 2009) and social skills training (Kurtz & Mueser, 2008), to .3–.6 for various types of neurocognitive therapy (Wykes, Huddy, Cellard, McGurk, & Czobor, 2011), to .6–.9 for social cognitive interventions (Wykes et al., 2011). Effect sizes generally fall within the medium size range, with larger effect sizes when the outcome variable is more proximal to the treatment type, e.g., performance on neuropsychological tests is more proximal to neurocognitive therapy than social functioning or quality of life.

Research on real world effectiveness of psychiatric rehabilitation modalities has only recently begun to appear, and it is premature to draw any conclusions, except that the sheer difficulty of doing effectiveness studies reflects serious problems in dissemination and implementation outside of research settings. Similarly, although at least one meta-analysis has indicated synergistic effects in arrays of modalities (McGurk, Twamley et al., 2007), little is known about the effects of integrated multimodal programs.

The national multi-site trial of first-episode treatment (RAISE; discussed in Section 1.4.1) is a possibly precedent-setting effort to incorporate both efficacy and effectiveness questions in controlled research studies. RAISE was designed to use local resources to fund and deliver its treatment packages in real world mental health service settings. The treatment package included modalities that had strong evidence for efficacy, but which had never been validated for the first episode population outside major research centers. The positive outcomes of the RAISE project therefore speak directly to the question of effectiveness. A joint dissemination project, a collaboration of NIMH and SAMSHA, is currently underway and may show that the coordinated approach to efficacy and effectiveness accelerates adoption of new treatments in the real world.

4.4   Variations and Combinations of Methods

The multimodal nature of psychiatric rehabilitation demands continuous variation and combination of modalities. As the toolbox expands, it becomes less feasible for a single team or even agency to provide the full array of services. Different parts of the array are critical to different settings and subpopulations, e.g., institutional vs. community, residential vs. outpatient, occupational/vocational programs, first episode/early intervention programs, programs for veterans or seniors. Different organizational models (discussed in Section 4.1.15) are amenable to different parts of the complete array. In addition, adaption of evidence-based modalities to particular cultural or racial/ethnic subpopulations may prove important, although research on this has only just begun (e.g., Weisman de Mamani et al., 2014). At the level of the individual undergoing rehabilitation and recovery, personal preferences and goals require further personalization of the individual treatment and rehabilitation plan. Approaches for accomplishing this are discussed in Section 3.

4.5   Problems in Carrying Out the Treatment

The biggest problem in application of treatment and rehabilitation for the schizophrenia spectrum is undoubtedly *dissemination*, the process by which new methods and technologies become available to consumers. There are five domains of activity especially pertinent to dissemination: (1) review and meta-analysis of the research, (2) formulation of social policy, (3) creation of funding streams and promulgation of regulations, (4) education and training of practitioners, and (5) the economics of the provider industry. Barriers to dissemination occur in all five domains.

4.5.1   The Domain of Research Review and Meta-Analysis

Research review and meta-analysis occurs at all levels of science, but concern about evidence-based practice has stimulated a research review industry specialized for informing clinical application and social policy. In the United States, the best example relevant to the schizophrenia spectrum has been the Schizophrenia Patient Outcomes Research Team (PORT) project, based at the University of Maryland. PORT began publishing major reviews and recommendations in the late 1990s with subsequent updates (e.g., Dickerson & Lehman, 2011). In the UK a comparable example is the Cochrane organization (e.g., Naeem, Farooq, & Kingdon, 2015).

The PORT reports are snapshots in the history of the treatment and rehabilitation research over the past 15 years. Collectively, the reports express unrequited optimism about new pharmacological treatments, lingering skepticism about psychological treatment, and consistent acknowledgement of the need for non-treatment support services such as ACT and supported employment. This has not been particularly conducive to dissemination of psychiatric rehabilitation. Over time, however, there has been a trend toward greater acceptance of psychological approaches and modalities and their role in recovery. Conclusions are somewhat obscured by shifting terminology as categories of treatment evolve in the course of research, e.g., the fluid boundary between neurocognitive and other cognitive and behavioral approaches (discussed in Sections 4.1.3 and 4.1.4). The more recent PORT reports are appropriately circumspect about this, recognizing on the one hand that modalities may diversify while retaining the same active ingredients, but on the other that old categories should not necessarily subsume superficially similar approaches if the outcomes and active ingredients are qualitatively different.

It may seem obvious that evidence-based practices should be based on active ingredients and outcomes, not packaging or other embellishments, but the two are not always distinguished in the policy discourse. Similarly, there are too few studies of complete, integrated service system arrays to provide credible effect size estimates for comprehensive high quality psychiatric rehabilitation vs. *treatment as usual*. As a result, the findings in these reviews do not translate directly into effective policy or regulation. Individual modalities are funded seemingly arbitrarily. For example, in some states neurocognitive therapy or cognitive remediation requires a separate set of regulatory definitions, but in others it is reimbursed under the rubric of psychotherapy, and in others not at all, despite meta-analytic effect sizes. Reviews that do not identify the active ingredients of efficacy simply cannot meaningfully inform policy.

4.5.2   Mental Health Policy, Funding, and Regulation

In national mental health policy the turn of the 21st century saw major developments relevant to dissemination and the schizophrenia spectrum. The US Congress had set the stage for the transformed view of mental illness as a disability with the *Americans with Disabilities Act of 1990*. In 1999 a report of the US Surgeon General issued a broad indictment of the national mental health system, especially its ability to serve those with severe and disabling conditions. In 2003 a President's Commission on Mental Health issued a report whose contents were summarized by the Commission chair: "After a year of study, and after reviewing research and testimony, the Commission finds that recovery from mental illness is now a real possibility" (President's New Freedom Commission on Mental Health, 2002). The US Congress passed the *Mental Health Parity and Addiction Equity Act of 2000,* intending to end discrimination in the healthcare insurance industry. However, these expressions of social and political support for psychiatric rehabilitation and recovery did not necessarily enhance the process of translating efficacious research procedures into effective practices. In 2014 the Substance Abuse and Mental Health Administration (SAMHSA) was criticized by the Government Accountability Office for neglecting the needs of people with the most severe conditions and disabilities (U. S. Government Accountability Office, 2014). The PORT reports during this period also identified dissemination of well-supported new treatment for the schizophrenia spectrum as slower than in other areas of healthcare, including pharmacological and psychosocial treatments.

Slow translation of policy into funding and regulation is also a barrier to dissemination. Even congressional mandates, e.g., the 2008 federal insurance parity law, have not yet substantially affected dissemination of psychiatric rehabilitation. Similarly, the Affordable Care Act of 2010 is transforming the American healthcare and healthcare underwriting industries, but it remains unclear what effect it will have on people with schizophrenia spectrum disorders. After all, underwriting general family health care is quite distinct from underwriting long-term disability, and services related to the schizophrenia spectrum fall in the latter category at least as much the former. Separate systems have evolved for disability, including death and dismemberment insurance and Social Security disability programs. The next few years will see upheaval in the insurance industry, resolution will be difficult, and dissemination will continue to be slow, as the finance mechanisms for general healthcare and psychiatric rehabilitation are sorted out.

4.5.3   Education and Training of Practitioners

Many psychologists have no interest and no training in working with patients who have schizophrenia spectrum disorders

Education and training of practitioners for the schizophrenia spectrum has historically been a major barrier to dissemination. Many new practitioners are not interested in working with the population and/or not adequately trained to implement effective services for them. Often they are prepared as generalists and are insufficiently familiar with the schizophrenia spectrum and psychiatric rehabilitation. Contributing to this problem is the very limited attention to severe and disabling mental illness in most graduate training programs (Mueser, Silverstein, & Farkas, 2013). The lack of interest among psychology graduate students is not well supported by data, but the limited opportunities to learn about the schizophrenia spectrum, psychiatric rehabilitation, or even interdisciplinary treatment teams is well supported (Reddy, Spaulding, Jansen, Menditto, & Pikett, 2010). It is incumbent upon graduate training programs in mental health disciplines to better address these issues and provide more training and clinical experience for students in the implementation of evidence-based practices in this area. A related barrier is the tendency of many clinicians to get most of their information about treatment from pharmaceutical company marketing materials (Bromley, 2005). This tendency leads to a failure to learn about effective psychological treatments and over-reliance on pharmacotherapy.

4.5.4   The Economics of the Mental Health Provider Industry

The institutional culture is a barrier to developing evidence-based practices in institutional settings. Deinstitutionalization reduced the number of residents of state psychiatric hospitals by about 90%, but the number of institutions decreased by only a third. By 2010 the downward trajectory had leveled off, at about 40,000 people in some 200 institutions across the country. The institutions are much smaller today, averaging about 200 beds. Their functions vary, with combinations of forensic and civilly committed patients, with intermediate to long-term length of treatment. Social learning programs (SLPs) are known to be by far the most cost-effective for these populations, but they are the exception rather than the rule in today's mental health systems. It has long been recognized (Liberman, 1979; Stuve & Menditto, 1999) that SLPs are inconsistent with the traditional organizational and professional hierarchies of psychiatric institutions, which modally operate on an institutional version of the medical model. A similar problem, but different in some respects, is created by the rapidly increasing need to treat schizophrenia spectrum disorders in the correctional system. SLPs bring a level of measurability and accountability not well tolerated by vested institutional interests. Institutions can and should be held accountable for using evidence-based practices, by appropriate regulation and oversight, and the consequences of administrative failure to manage opposing institutional interests can have far-reaching effects on the mental health system (Tarasenko et al., 2013).

Deinstitutionalization also created new challenges for dissemination in community-based mental health services. Although policy and planning called for creation of community mental health centers to serve the historical institutional population, less than half were actually built. The institutional culture inhibited migration of state hospital resources into the community, and the practitioners and direct care workers most experienced with the schizophrenia spectrum population remained somewhat separate from the community-based provider community. As resources formerly invested in the state hospitals became available to community providers, economic incentives further inhibited development of services best suited to the historical institutional population. Without sufficient regulation and oversight, people with schizophrenia spectrum disorders disproportionately become victims of "cherry picking", an element in the business model of some corporate providers, wherein the provider collects the revenues intended to follow the historical population into the community but uses the funding to serve its traditional community clientele, e.g., people with substance abuse and *co-occurring* anxiety, depression, or personality disorder. Dissemination thus depends on administrative accountability not only to provide evidence-based services, but also to provide them to the intended population (Spaulding & Sullivan, 2016b).

4.6   Multicultural Issues

For the practitioner, cultural factors in the schizophrenia spectrum generally have the most immediate impact when working with refugee or recent-immigrant populations, when key features of the person's native culture are first confronting the new culture. Cultural differences in stigmatization of mental illness are especially important considerations. The website of the American Psychological Association (see Resources section) includes relevant resources for practitioners. Although stigmatization of mental illness appears to occur in all cultures, there are sometimes dramatic differences that can affect a person's access to treatment and other forms of support. Cultural ideas about the nature of mental illness, about family responsibilities for the affected person, and about shame and family honor, require careful consideration in assessment, treatment planning, and rehabilitation. Such ideas are also variable *within* cul-

The stigma associated with mental illness varies widely across cultural groups

tures, so the practitioner must also avoid cultural stereotypes while assembling an individualized and culturally sensitive formulation.

Within western cultures, cultural diversity in recent immigrant populations becomes racial and ethnic diversity over the course of a few generations. Unfortunately, we understand very little about the role of racial and ethnic factors in etiology, because they are very difficult to distinguish from the effects of socioeconomic status, poverty, discrimination, trauma, and other socioenvironmental factors. For the practitioner, sensitivity to diversity in schizophrenia spectrum disorders is not different from sensitivity to such factors in other domains of mental health practice. Avoiding stereotypes about gender, sexual orientation, and related characteristics is no less important, but research has not identified considerations about this specific to the schizophrenia spectrum.

With the research in such an embryonic stage, the major diversity issue for the schizophrenia spectrum, at least within the United States, is *healthcare disparities,* and in particular, disparities in access to healthcare. People with schizophrenia spectrum disorders suffer especially poor access as a group, irrespective of age, gender, race, or ethnic identity (Wang, Demler, & Kessler, 2002). Indeed, having a disabling mental illness itself makes one a member of an abused and neglected minority.

5

Case Vignettes

It is impossible to portray a "typical" case vignette for schizophrenia spectrum disorders because of the extreme heterogeneity created by individual differences in age, gender, socioeconomic status, symptoms and other impairments, and other personal characteristics. We therefore describe two representative vignettes that illustrate the extremes of variability that the practitioner encounters in real world mental health settings.

Sally was a 20-year-old woman from a city in the eastern United States who developed auditory hallucinations and paranoid delusions during her junior year at a college on the west coast. After a period of increased marijuana use, declining concentration, increasing anxiety, social isolation, angry outbursts in public places (e.g., a cafeteria), and, eventually, paranoid thinking and auditory hallucinations, she was hospitalized for three weeks, during which time she began taking risperidone, an antipsychotic medication. After leaving the hospital, she withdrew from her university, returned to her parents' home, and developed a treatment relationship with an outpatient psychiatrist. Sally's hallucinations and paranoia were significantly reduced although still present at times. Her parents were encouraged by the reduction of inappropriate behavior, but gradually became concerned that Sally was not doing anything with her life. On a typical day she would sleep late, watch TV most of the day, not go out of the house, and then stay up late reading or smoking in her room. This led increasingly to interactions with her family in which they criticized her for being lazy and not "getting on with her life." The results of these stressful interactions were further withdrawal and increasing frustration on the part of her parents. In response to these issues, Sally's psychiatrist suggested that Sally meet with a psychologist for individual therapy and to help her move forward with her life. It was also suggested that the family attend family therapy, which they agreed to do. In a time-limited version of multiple family psychoeducation, Sally's family learned about schizophrenia, including negative symptoms and the importance of not blaming the patient for them, and about effective communication and conflict resolution skills. This gradually improved the environment in the home. Sally also began meeting with a psychologist once or twice a week. The initial focus of these meetings was to clarify Sally's short-term goals, which included returning to school and living independently. Sally enrolled in a local college and began taking a full course load, against the advice of her family and treatment providers. However, she soon found that her ability to focus on the lectures and readings was not at her premorbid level and she was occasionally distracted by hearing voices. She was therefore put in touch with supported education services at her school, and a counselor began working with her to promote study habits that would lead to maximum retention of information. She also eventually agreed to drop two of her courses. At this point, the focus of therapy shifted to her residual symptoms, to help her cope better with the voices, and to reduce anxiety and paranoia by recognizing attribution errors and generating more appropriate thoughts about interpersonal situations. A continuing issue, however, was Sally's desire to use marijuana. During periods of increased workload, or when considering going to social events at school, she would smoke in order to feel relaxed, although she often developed unusual thoughts and paranoia instead. Sally recognized that she had a problem and agreed to attend a 3 times per week dual-diagnosis group that used the UCLA Substance Abuse Management Module at a local mental health center. She received a great deal of social support from the group, as well as information about the adverse effects of marijuana on her psychiatric condition. Sally was eventually able to cut down her marijuana use significantly and continued to pursue her personal and educational goals.

John spent most of his adult life in psychiatric hospitals. He was continuously hospitalized from the early 1960s until 1989 when he was enrolled in a comprehensive social learning program (SLP) modeled closely on that described by Paul and Lentz (1977). By this time he had been residing in a maximum-security psychiatric facility for 20 years due to severe schizophrenia and episodes of violence. At the time he was admitted to the SLP, he was mostly mute, speaking only monosyllabically when attempting to get his needs met. He exhibited behaviors suggestive of auditory hallucinations and delusions, his self-care and social skills were very poor, and he was often aggressive and sexually inappropriate. He was enrolled in attention shaping classes and a full array of skills training groups and activities all supported by ongoing behavioral shaping and reinforcement procedures. While still residing in maximum security, it was noted that he enjoyed cleaning during weekend housekeeping activities, and he was given a job cleaning the facility dining room after lunch each day. He became more social, his self-care improved markedly, he exhibited fewer bizarre behaviors, and his aggression reduced to zero instances. After several years he progressed to a step down inpatient unit and then to a community-based group home both offering comprehensive rehabilitation services based on the social learning model. While residing in the group home, he worked as a janitor at the state Department of Mental Health headquarters, and he realized one of his most cherished recovery goals—to attend a professional baseball game. He continued to reside in the community for nearly 10 years without the need for rehospitalization prior to his death from natural causes.

6

Further Reading

Annoted suggestions for further reading on schizophrenia spectrum disorders, treatment and rehabilitation, and resources for families and practitioners.

Amador, X., & Johanson, A. (2000). *I am not sick I don't need help: Helping the seriously mentally ill accept treatment*. Peconic, NY: Vida Press.
A monograph on the problem of impaired insight into need for treatment.

Bellack, A., Mueser, K., Gingerich, S., & Agresta, J. (2004). *Social skills training for schizophrenia: A step-by-step guide* (2nd ed.). New York, NY: Guilford Press.
A user-friendly guide and set of materials for conducting one of the most versatile and useful of the psychiatric rehabilitation modalities.

Castle, D., Copolov, T., Wykes, T. & Mueser, K. (Eds.). (2012) *Pharmacological and psychosocial treatment of schizophrenia* (3rd ed.). London, UK: Taylor & Francis. http://doi.org/10.3109/9781842145357
An international perspective with balanced representation across the range of biosystemic levels of functioning, compact and pragmatically oriented.

Davidson, L. (2003). *Living outside mental illness: Qualitative studies of recovery in schizophrenia*. New York, NY: New York University Press.
Pioneering monograph about the experience of people with schizophrenia as they begin to move beyond seeing themselves as patients, and toward more meaningful identities.

Hagen, R., Turkington, D., Berge, T., & Gråwe, R. W. (Eds.). (2011). *CBT for psychosis: A symptom-based approach*. New York, NY: Routledge/Taylor & Francis Group.
Building on decades of previous research and clinical experience, this is a guide for using cognitive behavioral therapy focused on symptoms and other features of psychosis.

Li, M., & Spaulding, W. (Eds.). (2016). *The Nebraska Symposium on Motivation: Vol 63. The neuropsychopathology of schizophrenia: Molecules, brain systems, motivation, and cognition*. London, UK: Springer.
Cutting edge views of the schizophrenia spectrum in the new biosystemic paradigm, in a volume of the oldest continuously-running theoretical forum in psychology.

Liberman, R. (2008). *Recovery from disability: Manual of psychiatric rehabilitation*. Arlington, VA: American Psychiatric Publishing.
A comprehensive account by one of the field's founding figures.

Mueser, K. T., Noordsy, D. L., Drake, R. E., & Fox, L. (2003). *Integrated treatment for dual disorders: A guide to effective practice*. New York, NY: Guilford.
Comprehensive summary of all important treatment components involved in treating dually diagnosed clients, including discussions of assessment, individual, group, family, and residential approaches, and motivational interviewing, along with many useful handouts and tools.

Sass, L. (1992). *Madness and modernism*. Cambridge, MA: Harvard University Press.
A fascinating description of the inner world of many schizophrenia patients, using insights drawn from phenomenological philosophy.

Singh, N., Barber, J. & Van Sant, S. (Eds.). (2016). *Handbook of recovery in inpatient psychiatry*. London, UK: Springer. http://doi.org/10.1007/978-3-319-40537-7
A comprehensive update of treatment and rehabilitation in hospital settings in the era of recovery.

Spaulding, W., Sullivan, M., & Poland, J. (2003). *Treatment and rehabilitation of severe mental illness*. New York, NY: Guilford.

A comprehensive synthesis of psychopathology and psychiatric rehabilitation in the biosystemic paradigm.

Whitaker, R. (2003). *Mad in America: Bad science, bad medicine, and the enduring mistreatment of the mentally ill*. Cambridge, MA: Perseus. Whitaker, R., & Cosgrove, L. (2015) *Psychiatry under the influence: Institutional corruption, social injury, and prescriptions for reform*. London, UK: Palgrave Macmillan.

Scathing indictments of the medical model and the pharmaceutical industry. The 2003 book focuses on schizophrenia. The 2015 book has a more sweeping scope.

Reddy, R., & Keshavan, M. S. (2015). *Understanding schizophrenia: A practical guide for patients, families, and health care professionals*. Santa Barbara, CA: Praeger/ABC-CLIO.

A brief overview and synthesis, mostly for a lay audience.

7

References

Aas, M., Djurovic, S., Athanasiu, L., Steen, N. E., Agartz, I., Lorentzen, S., . . . Melle, I. (2012). Serotonin transporter gene polymorphism, childhood trauma, and cognition in patients with psychotic disorders. *Schizophrenia Bulletin, 38*(1), 15–22. http://doi.org/10.1093/schbul/sbr113

Allness, D., & Knoedler, W. (2003). *The PACT model of community-based treatment for persons with severe and persistent mental illnesses: A manual for PACT start-up.* Arlington, VA: National Alliance for the Mentally Ill.

American Psychological Association. (2015). *Policy statement on evidence-based practice in psychology.* Retrieved from http://www.apa.org/practice/guidelines/evidence-based-statement.aspx

American Psychiatric Association. (2013). *Diagnostic and statistical manual for mental disorders* (5th ed.). Washington, DC: Author.

Andreasen, N. C. (1984). *The broken brain: The biological revolution in psychiatry.* New York, NY: Harper.

Anthony, W., Buell, G., Sharratt, S., & Althoff, M. (1972). Efficacy of psychiatric rehabilitation. *Psychological Bulletin, 78,* 447–456. http://doi.org/10.1037/h0033743

August, S. M., Kiwanuka, J. N., McMahon, R. P., & Gold, J. M. (2012). The MATRICS Consensus Cognitive Battery (MCCB): Clinical and cognitive correlates. *Schizophrenia Research, 134*(1), 76–82. http://doi.org/10.1016/j.schres.2011.10.015

Ayllon, T., & Azrin, N. H. (1968). *The token economy.* New York, NY: Appleton-Century-Crofts.

Bach, P., Hayes, S. C., & Gallop, R. (2012). Long-term effects of brief acceptance and commitment therapy for psychosis. *Behavior Modification, 36*(2), 165–181. http://doi.org/10.1177/0145445511427193

Bacon, T., Farhall, J., & Fossey, E. (2014). The Active Therapeutic Processes of Acceptance and Commitment Therapy for Persistent Symptoms of Psychosis: Clients' Perspectives. *Behavioral and Cognitive Psychotherapy, 42,* 402–420. http://doi.org/10.1017/S1352465813000209

Baldwin, L., Beck, N., Menditto, A., Arms, T., & Cormier, J. F. (1992). Decreasing excessive water drinking by chronic mentally ill forensic patients. *Hospital and Community Psychiatry, 43,* 507–509.

Barch, D. M. (2010). Pharmacological strategies for enhancing cognition in schizophrenia. *Current Topics in Behavioral Neuroscience, 4,* 43–96. http://doi.org/10.1007/7854_2010_39

Bechdolf, A., Pohlmann, B., Güttgemanns, J., Geyer, C., Lindner, K., Ferber, C., & Gouzoulis-Mayfrank, E. (2012). Motivationsbehandlung für Patienten mit der Doppeldiagnose Psychose und Sucht: Ergebnisse einer randomisierten Studie [Motivational interviewing for patients with the dual diagnosis of psychosis and addiction: Results of a randomized study]. *Der Nervenarzt, 83*(7), 888–896. http://doi.org/10.1007/s00115-011-3331-6

Beck, N. C., Menditto, A. A., Baldwin, L., Angelone, E., & Maddox, M. (1991). Reduced frequency of aggressive behavior in forensic patients in a social learning program. *Hospital and Community Psychiatry, 42,* 750–752.

Bellack, A. S., Brown, C., & Thomas-Loorman, S. (2006). Psychometric characteristics of role-play assessments of social skill in schizophrenia. *Behavior Therapy, 37,* 339–352.

Bellack, A., Mueser, K., Gingerich, S., & Agresta, J. (2004). *Social skills training for schizophrenia: A step-by-step guide* (2nd ed.). New York, NY: Guilford Press.

Bellack, A. S., Schooler, N. R, Marder, S. R., Kane, J. M., Brown, C. H., & Yang, Y. (2004). Do clozapine and risperidone affect social competence and problem solving? *American Journal of Psychiatry, 161,* 364–367. http://doi.org/10.1176/appi.ajp.161.2.364

Berg, A. O., Aas, M., Larsson, S., Nerhus, M., Hauff, E., Andreassen, O. A., & Melle, I. (2015). Childhood trauma mediates the association between ethnic minority status and more severe hallucinations in psychotic disorder. *Psychological Medicine, 45*(1), 133–142. http://doi.org/10.1017/S0033291714001135

Berthelot, N., Paccalet, T., Gilbert, E., Moreau, I., Mérette, C., Gingras, N., . . . Maziade, M. (2015). Childhood abuse and neglect may induce deficits in cognitive precursors of psychosis in high-risk children. *Journal of Psychiatry & Neuroscience, 40*(5), 336–343. http://doi.org/10.1503/jpn.140211

Böker, W., & Brenner, H. D. (1983). Selbstheilungsversuche Schizophrener [Attempts to self-heal from schizophrenia]. *Nervenarzt, 54,* 578–589.

Bond, G., Dincin, J., Setze, P., & Witheridge, T. (1984). The effectiveness of psychiatric rehabilitation: A summary of research at thresholds. *Psychosocial Rehabilitation Journal, 7,* 6–22.

Bromley, E. (2005). A collaborative approach to targeted treatment development for schizophrenia: A qualitative evaluation of the NIMH-MATRICS project. *Schizophrenia Bulletin, 31,* 954–961. http://doi.org/10.1093/schbul/sbi059

Buican, B., Spaulding, W., Gordon, B., & Hindman, T. (1999). Clinical decision support systems in state hospitals. In W. Spaulding (Ed.), *The role of the state hospital in the 21st century* (Vol. 84, pp. 99–112). San Francisco, CA: Jossey-Bass.

Cancel, A., Comte, M., Truillet, R., Boukezzi, S., Rousseau, P. F., Zendjidjian, X. Y., . . . Fakra, E. (2015). Childhood neglect predicts disorganization in schizophrenia through grey matter decrease in dorsolateral prefrontal cortex. *Acta Psychiatrica Scandinavica, 132*(4), 244–256. http://doi.org/10.1111/acps.12455

Cook, J. A., Copeland, M. E., Jonikas, J. A., Hamilton, M. M., Razzano, L. A., Grey, D. D., . . . Boyd, S. (2012). Results of a randomized controlled trial of mental illness self-management using Wellness Recovery Action Planning. *Schizophrenia Bulletin, 38*(4), 881–891. http://doi.org/10.1093/schbul/sbr012

Copeland, M. E. (1997). *Wellness recovery action plan.* West Dummerston, VT: Peach Press.

Corrigan, P., Mueser, K., Bond, G., Drake, R., & Solomon, P. (2008). *Principles and practice of psychiatric rehabilitation: An empirical approach.* New York, NY: Guilford Press.

Cromwell, R. L. (1975). Assessment of schizophrenia. *Annual Review of Psychology, 26,* 593–619. http://doi.org/10.1146/annurev.ps.26.020175.003113

Daly, B. P., Hildenbrand, A. K., & Brown, R. T. (2016). *Attention-deficit / hyperactivity disorder in children and adolescents.* Boston, MA: Hogrefe.

DeSisto, M., Harding, C. M., McCormick, R. V., Ashikaga, T., & Brooks, G. W. (1995a). The Maine and Vermont three-decade studies of serious mental illness. II. Longitudinal course comparisons. *British Journal of Psychiatry, 167,* 338–342. http://doi.org/10.1192/bjp.167.3.338

Dickerson, F. B., & Lehman, A. F. (2011). Evidence-based psychotherapy for schizophrenia: 2011 update. *Journal of Nervous and Mental Disease, 199*(8), 520–526. http://doi.org/10.1097/NMD.0b013e318225ee78

Duckworth, K., & Halpern, L. (2014). Peer support and peer-led family support for persons living with schizophrenia. *Current Opinion in Psychiatry, 27,* 216–221.

Engstrom, E., & Kendler, K. (2015). Emil Kraepelin: Icon and reality. *American Journal of Psychiatry, 172*(12), 1190–1196. http://doi.org/10.1176/appi.ajp.2015.15050665

Epstein, K. A., & Kumra, S. (2014). Executive attention impairment in adolescents with schizophrenia who have used cannabis. *Schizophrenia Research, 157*(1–3), 48–54. http://doi.org/10.1016/j.schres.2014.04.035

Fairweather, G., Sanders, D., Maynard, H., & Cressler, D. (1969). *Community life for the mentally ill: An alternative to institutional care.* Chicago, IL: Aldine.

Feeney, T. J., & Ylvisaker, M. (2003). Context-sensitive behavioral supports for young children with TBI: Short-term effects and long-term outcome. *Journal of Head Trauma Rehabilitation, 18,* 33–51. http://doi.org/10.1097/00001199-200301000-00006

Fish, B. (1987). Infant predictors of the longitudinal course of schizophrenic development. *Schizophrenia Bulletin, 13*, 395–409. http://doi.org/10.1093/schbul/13.3.395

Fisher, H. L., Jones, P. B., Fearon, P., Craig, T. K., Dazzan, P., Morgan, K., . . . Morgan, C. (2010). The varying impact of type, timing and frequency of exposure to childhood adversity on its association with adult psychotic disorder. *Psychological Medicine, 40*(12), 1967–1978. http://doi.org/10.1017/S0033291710000231

Fisher, S. H., & Beard, J. H. (1962). Fountain house: A psychiatric rehabilitation program. *Current Psychiatric Therapeutics, 2*, 211–218.

Fiszdon, J. M., & Bell, M. D. (2004). Remédiation cognitive et thérapie occupationnelle dans le traitement ambulatoire du patient souffrant de schizophrénie [Cognitive remediation and work therapy in the outpatient treatment of patients with schizophrenia]. *Santé Mentale au Québec, 29*, 117–142. http://doi.org/10.7202/010834ar

French, L., Gray, C., Leonard, G., Perron, M., Pike, G. B., Richer, L., . . . Paus, T. (2015). Early cannabis use, polygenic risk score for schizophrenia and brain maturation in adolescence. *JAMA Psychiatry, 72*, 1002–1011. http://doi.org/10.1001/jamapsychiatry.2015.1131

Friston, K. J., Stephan, K. E., Montague, R., & Dolan, R. J. (2014). Computational psychiatry: The brain as a phantastic organ. *Lancet Psychiatry, 1*(2), 148–158. http://doi.org/10.1016/S2215-0366(14)70275-5

D'Zurilla, T. J., & Goldfried, M. R. (1971). Problem solving and behavior modification. *Journal of Abnormal Psychology, 78*(1), 107–126. http://doi.org/10.1037/h0031360

Granholm, E., Holden, J., Link, P. C., & McQuaid, J. R. (2014). Randomized clinical trial of cognitive behavioral social skills training for schizophrenia: Improvement in functioning and experiential negative symptoms. *Journal of Consulting and Clinical Psychology, 82*(6), 1173–1185. http://doi.org/10.1037/a0037098

Guo, X., Zhai, J., Liu, Z., Fang, M., Wang, B., Wang, C., . . . Zhao, J. (2010). Effect of antipsychotic medication alone vs combined with psychosocial intervention on outcomes of early-stage schizophrenia: A randomized, 1-year study. *Archives of General Psychiatry, 67*, 895–904. http://doi.org/10.1001/archgenpsychiatry.2010.105

Harder, S., Koester, A., Valbak, K., & Rosenbaum, B. (2014). Five-year follow-up of supportive psychodynamic psychotherapy in first-episode psychosis: Long-term outcome in social functioning. *Psychiatry, 77*(2), 155–168. http://doi.org/10.1521/psyc.2014.77.2.155

Harding, C. M., Brooks, G. W., Ashikaga, T., Strauss, J. S., & Breier, A. (1987). The Vermont longitudinal study of persons with severe mental illness, II: Long-term outcome of subjects who retrospectively met DSM-III criteria for schizophrenia. *American Journal of Psychiatry, 144*, 727–735.

Harrow, M., Jobe, T. H., & Faull, R. N. (2014). Does treatment of schizophrenia with antipsychotic medications eliminate or reduce psychosis? A 20-year multi-follow-up study. *Psychological Medicine, 44*, 3007–3016. http://doi.org/10.1017/S0033291714000610

Harvey, P. D., & Bowie, C. R. (2012). Cognitive remediation in severe mental illness. *Innovations in Clinical Neuroscience, 9*(4), 27–30.

Heilbrun, A. (1973). *Aversive maternal control: A theory of schizophrenic development.* New York, NY: Wiley.

Hobart, M. P., Goldberg, R., Bartko, J. J., & Gold, J. M. (1999). Repeatable battery for the assessment of neuropsychological status as a screening test in schizophrenia, II: convergent/ discriminant validity and diagnostic group comparisons. *American Journal of Psychiatry, 156*, 1951–1957.

Hogarty, G. E., Flesher, S., Ulrich, R., Carter, M., Greenwald, D., Pogue-Geile, M., . . . Zoretich, R. (2004). Cognitive enhancement therapy for schizophrenia: Effects of a 2-year randomized trial on cognition and behavior. *Archives of General Psychiatry, 61*, 866–876.

Hogarty, G., Greenwald, D., Ulrich, R., Kornblith, S., DiBarry, A., Cooley, S., . . . Flesher, S. (1997). Three-year trials of personal therapy among schizophrenic patients living with or independent of family: II. Effects of adjustment of patients. *American Journal of Psychiatry, 154*(11), 1514–1524. http://doi.org/10.1176/ajp.154.11.1514

Hogarty, G. E., & Ulrich, R. F. (1998). The limitations of antipsychotic medication on schizophrenia relapse and adjustment and the contributions of psychosocial treatment. *Journal of Psychiatric Research, 32*(3–4), 243–250. http://doi.org/10.1016/S0022-3956(97)00013-7

Hopper, K., Harrison, G., Janca, A., & Sartorius, N. (2007). *Recovery from schizophrenia: An international perspective: A report from the WHO Collaborative Project, the international study of schizophrenia.* New York, NY: Oxford University Press.

IAPSRS: International Association of Psychosocial Rehabilitation Services. (1997). *Practice guidelines for the psychiatric rehabilitation of persons with severe and persistent mental illness in a managed care environment.* Columbia, MD: Author.

Hunter, R. H., Wilkniss, S., Gardner, W., & Silverstein, S. M. (2008). The multimodal functional model – Advancing case formulation beyond the 'diagnose and treat' paradigm: Improving outcomes and reducing aggression and the use of control procedures in psychiatric care. *Psychological Services, 5*, 11–25. http://doi.org/10.1037/1541-1559.5.1.11

Insel, T. R. (2008). Assessing the economic costs of serious mental illness. *The American Journal of Psychiatry, 165*(6), 663–665. http://doi.org/10.1176/appi.ajp.2008.08030366

Jääskeläinen, E., Juola, P., Hirvonen, N., McGrath, J. J., Saha, S., Isohanni, M., . . . Miettunen, J. (2013). A systematic review and meta-analysis of recovery in schizophrenia. *Schizophrenia Bulletin, 39*(6), 1296–1306. http://doi.org/10.1093/schbul/sbs130

Jauhar, S., McKenna, P. J., Radua, J., Fung, E., Salvador, R., & Laws, K. R. (2014). Cognitive-behavioural therapy for the symptoms of schizophrenia: Systematic review and meta-analysis with examination of potential bias. *British Journal of Psychiatry, 204*(1), 20–29. http://doi.org/10.1192/bjp.bp.112.116285

Jobe, T. H., & Harrow, M. (2005). Long-term outcome of patients with schizophrenia: A review. *Canadian Journal of Psychiatry, 50*(14), 892–900.

Kahn, R. S., Fleischhacker, W. W., Boter, H., Davidson, M., Vergouwe, Y., Keet, I. P., . . . Grobbee, D. E. (2008). Effectiveness of antipsychotic drugs in first-episode schizophrenia and schizophreniform disorder: An open randomised clinical trial. *Lancet, 371*, 1085–1097. http://doi.org/10.1016/S0140-6736(08)60486-9

Kane, J. M, Robinson, D., Schooler, N., Mueser, K., Penn, D., Rosenheck, R. A., . . . Heinssen, R. (2016). Comprehensive versus usual community care for first-episode psychosis: 2-year outcomes from the NIMH RAISE early treatment program. *American Journal of Psychiatry, 173,* 362–372. doi: 10.1176/appi.ajp.2015.15050632 http://doi.org/10.1176/appi.ajp.2015.15050632

Kavanagh, D. J., McGrath, J., Saunders, J. B., Dore, G., & Clark, D. (2002). Substance misuse in patients with schizophrenia: Epidemiology and management. *Drugs, 62,* 743–755. http://doi.org/10.2165/00003495-200262050-00003

Keefe, R. S., Davis, V. G., Spagnola, N. B., Hilt, D., Dgetluck, N., Ruse, S., . . . Harvey, P. D. (2015). Reliability, validity and treatment sensitivity of the Schizophrenia Cognition Rating Scale. *European Neuropsychopharmacology, 25*(2), 176–184. http://doi.org/10.1016/j.euroneuro.2014.06.009

Keefe, R. S., Goldberg, T. E., Harvey, P. D., Gold, J. M., Poe, M. P., & Coughenour, L. (2004). The Brief Assessment of Cognition in Schizophrenia: reliability, sensitivity, and comparison with a standard neurocognitive battery. *Schizophrenia Research, 68,* 283–297. http://doi.org/10.1016/j.schres.2003.09.011

Kelly, T., Daley, D., & Douaihy, A. (2012). Treatment of substance abusing patients with comorbid psychiatric disorders. *Addictive Behavior, 37,* 11–24. http://doi.org/10.1016/j.addbeh.2011.09.010

Kern, R. S., Green, M. F., Mitchell, S., Kopelowicz, A., Mintz, J., & Liberman, R. P. (2005). Extensions of errorless learning for social problem-solving deficits in schizophrenia. *American Journal of Psychiatry, 162,* 513–519. http://doi.org/10.1176/appi.ajp.162.3.513

Khoury, B., Lecomte, T., Gaudiano, B. A., & Paquin, K. (2013). Mindfulness interventions for psychosis: A meta-analysis. *Schizophrenia Research, 150*(1), 176–184. http://doi.org/10.1016/j.schres.2013.07.055

Klein, D. (1980). Psychosocial treatment of schizophrenia, or psychosocial help for people with schizophrenia? *Schizophrenia Bulletin, 6*(1), 122–130. http://doi.org/10.1093/schbul/6.1.122

Klingberg, S., Wittorf, A., Fischer, A., Jakob-Deters, K., Buchremer, G., & Wiedemann, G. (2010). Evaluation of a cognitive behaviourally oriented service for relapse prevention in schizophrenia. *Acta Psychiatrica Scandinavica, 121*, 340–350. http://doi.org/10.1111/j.1600-0447.2009.01479.x

Kurtz, M. M., & Mueser, K. T. (2008). A meta-analysis of controlled research on social skills training for schizophrenia. *Journal of Consulting and Clinical Psychology, 76*(3), 491–504. http://doi.org/10.1037/0022-006X.76.3.491

Kutchins, H., & Kirk, S. (1997). *Making us crazy: The psychiatric bible and the creation of psychiatric disorders*. New York, NY: Free Press.

Leucht, S., Arbter, D., Engel, R., Kissling, W., & Davis, J. (2009). How effective are second-generation antipsychotic drugs? A meta-analysis of placebo-controlled trials. *Molecular Psychiatry, 14*(4), 429–447. http://doi.org/10.1038/sj.mp.4002136

Lewis, D., & Glausier, J. (2016). Alteration in prefrontal cortical circuitry and cognitive dysfunction in schizophrenia. In M. Li & W. Spaulding (Eds.), *The neuropsychopathology of schizophrenia: Modecules, brain systems, motivation and cognition* (pp. 31–75). New York, NY: Springer.

Liberman, R. P. (1979). Social and political challenges to the development of behavioral programs in organizations. In P. O. Sjoden, I. W. S. Dockens, & S. Bates (Eds.), *Trends in behavior therapy* (pp. 369–398). New York, NY: Academic Press.

Liberman, R. P. (2008). *Recovery from disability: Manual of psychiatric rehabilitation*. Washington, DC: American Psychiatric Press.

Liberman, R. P., Glynn, S., Blair, K. E., Ross, D., & Marder, S. R. (2002). In vivo amplified skills training: Promoting generalization of independent living skills for clients with schizophrenia. *Psychiatry: Interpersonal and Biological Processes, 65*(2), 137–155. http://doi.org/10.1521/psyc.65.2.137.19931

Liberman, R. P., Gutkind, D., Mintz, J., Green, M., Marshall, B. D., Jr., Robertson, M. J., & Hayden, J. (2002). Impact of risperidone versus haloperidol on activities of daily living in the treatment of refractory schizophrenia. *Comprehensive Psychiatry, 43*(6), 469–473. http://doi.org/10.1053/comp.2002.33499

Lincoln, T. M., Ziegler, M., Mehl, S., Kesting, M. L., Lullmann, E., Westermann, S., & Rief, W. (2012). Moving from efficacy to effectiveness in cognitive behavioral therapy for psychosis: a randomized clinical practice trial. *Journal of Consulting and Clinical Psychology, 80*(4), 674–686. http://doi.org/10.1037/a0028665

Lysaker, P. H., Glynn, S. M., Wilkniss, S. M., & Silverstein, S. M. (2010). Psychotherapy and recovery from schizophrenia: A review of potential applications and need for future study. *Psychological Services, 7*, 75–91. http://doi.org/10.1037/a0019115

Lysaker, P. H., Vohs, J., Minor, K. S., Irarrázaval, L., Leonhardt, B., Hamm, J. A., . . . Dimaggio, G. (2015). Metacognitive deficits in schizophrenia: Presence and associations with psychosocial outcomes. *Journal of Nervous and Mental Disease, 203*(7), 530–536. http://doi.org/10.1097/NMD.0000000000000323

Maher, B. A. (1988). Delusions as the product of normal cognitions. In T. F. Oltmanns & B. A. Maher (Eds.), *Delusional beliefs* (pp. 333–336). Oxford, UK: John Wiley & Sons.

Marcopulos, B. A., & Kurtz, M. M. (2012). *Clinical neuropsychological foundations of schizophrenia*. New York, NY: Psychology Press.

McGurk, S. R., Mueser, K. T., Feldman, K., Wolfe, R., & Pascaris, A. (2007). Cognitive training for supported employment: 2-3 year outcomes of a randomized controlled trial. *American Journal of Psychiatry, 164*(3), 437–441. http://doi.org/10.1176/ajp.2007.164.3.437

McGurk, S. R., Twamley, E. W., Sitzer, D. I., McHugo, G. J., & Mueser, K. T. (2007). A meta-analysis of cognitive remediation in schizophrenia. *American Journal of Psychiatry, 164*(12), 1791–1802. http://doi.org/10.1176/appi.ajp.2007.07060906

Medalia, A., & Brekke, J. (2010). In search of a theoretical structure for understanding motivation in schizophrenia. *Schizophrenia Bulletin, 36*, 912–918. http://doi.org/10.1093/schbul/sbq073

Medalia, A., Revheim, N., & Casey, M. (2001). The remediation of problem-solving skills in schizophrenia. *Schizophrenia Bulletin, 27*, 259–267. http://doi.org/10.1093/oxford-journals.schbul.a006872

Meier, S. M., Agerbo, E., Maier, R., Pedersen, C. B., Lang, M., Grove, J., . . . Mattheisen, M. (2016). High loading of polygenic risk in cases with chronic schizophrenia. *Molecular psychiatry, 21*, 969–974. http://doi.org/10.1038/mp.2015.130

Menditto, A. A., Beck, N. C., Stuve, P., Fisher, J. A., Stacy, M., Logue, M. B., & Baldwin, L.J. (1996). Effectiveness of clozapine and a social learning program for severely disabled psychiatric inpatients. *Psychiatric Services, 47*, 46–51.

Menditto, A. A., Wallace, C. J., Liberman, R. P., VanderWal, J., Jones, N. T., & Stuve, P. (1999). Functional assessment of independent living skills. *Psychiatric Rehabilitation Skills, 3*, 200–219. http://doi.org/10.1080/10973439908408384

Miller, W., & .Rollnick, S. (2002). *Motivational interviewing: Preparing people to change.* New York, NY: Guilford.

Mojtabai, R., Nicholson, R. A., Isohanni, M., Jones, P., & Partennen, U. (1998). Role of psychosocial treatments in management of schizophrenia: A meta-analytic review of controlled outcome studies. *Schizophrenia Bulletin, 24*, 569–587. http://doi.org/10.1093/oxfordjournals.schbul.a033350

Monnat, S. M., & Chandler, R. F. (2015). Long-term physical health consequences of adverse childhood experiences. *The Sociological Quarterly, 56*(4), 723–752. http://doi.org/10.1111/tsq.12107

Moriana, J. A., Alarcón, E., & Herruzo, J. (2006). In-home psychosocial skills training for patients with schizophrenia. *Psychiatric Services, 57*(2), 260–262. http://doi.org/10.1176/appi.ps.57.2.260

Mosher, L. R., & Bola, J. R. (2000). The Soteria Project: Twenty-five years of swimming upriver. *Complexity and Change, 9*, 68–74.

Mueser, K. T., Clark, R. E., Haines, M., Drake, R. E., McHugo, G. J., Bond, G. R., . . . Swain, K. (2004). The Hartford study of supported employment for persons with severe mental illness. *Journal of Consulting and Clinical Psychology, 72*, 479–490.

Mueser, K. T., & Gingerich, S. (2013). Treatment of co-occurring psychotic and substance use disorders. *Social Work and Public Health, 28*(3–4), 424–439. http://doi.org/10.1080/19371918.2013.774676

Mueser, K. T., Pratt, S. I., Bartels, S. J., Swain, K., Forester, B., Cather, C., & Feldman, J. (2010). Randomized trial of social rehabilitation and integrated health care for older people with severe mental illness. *Journal of Consulting and ClinicalPsychology, 78*(4), 561–573. http://doi.org/10.1037/a0019629

Mueser, K. T., Silverstein, S. M., & Farkas, M. D. (2013). Should the training of clinical psychologists require competence in the treatment and rehabilitation of individuals with a serious mental illness? *Psychiatric Rehabilitation Journal, 36*(1), 54–59. http://doi.org/10.1037/h0094750

Naeem, F., Farooq, S., & Kingdon, D. (2015). Cognitive behavioural therapy (brief versus standard duration) for schizophrenia. *Cochrane Database of Systematic Reviews, 10, Art. No.: CD010646*. Abstract retrieved from http://onlinelibrary.wiley.com/doi/10.1002/14651858.CD010646.pub3/abstract

Newbill, W. A., Paul, G. L., Menditto, A. A., Springer, J. R., & Mehta, P. (2011). Social-learning programs facilitate an increase in adaptive behavior in a forensic mental hospital. *Behavioral Interventions, 26*(3), 214–230. http://doi.org/10.1002/bin.330

Newton-Howes, G., & Wood, R. (2013). Cognitive-behavioral therapy and the psychopathology of schizophrenia: Systematic review and meta-analysis. *Psychology and Psychotherapy, 86*, 127–138. http://doi.org/10.1111/j.2044-8341.2011.02048.x

Nordgaard, J., & Parnas, J. (2014). Self-disorders and the schizophrenia spectrum: A study of 100 first hospital admissions. *Schizophrenia Bulletin, 40*, 1300–1307. http://doi.org/10.1093/schbul/sbt239

Ottavi, P., D'Alia, D., Lysaker, P., Kent, J., Popolo, R., Salvatore, G., & Dimaggio, G. (2014). Metacognition-oriented social skills training for individuals with long-term schizophrenia: Methodology and clinical illustration. *Clinical Psychology & Psychotherapy, 21*(5), 465–473. http://doi.org/10.1002/cpp.1850

Patterson, T. L., Goldman, S., McKibbin, C. L., Hughs, T., & Jeste, D. V. (2001). UCSD Performance- Based Skills Assessment: Development of a new measure of everyday functioning for severely mentally ill adults. *Schizophrenia Bulletin, 27*, 235–245. http://doi.org/10.1093/oxfordjournals.schbul.a006870

Paul, G. L. (Ed.). (1987). *Observational assessment instrumentation for service and research: The Time-Sample Behavioral Checklist for assessment in residential settings (Part 2).* Champaign, IL: Research Press.

Paul, G. L. (Ed.). (1988). *Observational assessment instrumentation for service and research: The Staff-Resident Interaction Chronograph: Assessment in residential treatment settings (Part 3).* Champaign, IL: Research Press.

Paul, G. L., & Lentz, R. J. (1977). *Psychosocial treatment of chronic mental patients: Milieu vs. social learning programs* 2nd ed. Cambridge, MA: Harvard University Press.

Phillips, W. A., Clark, A., & Silverstein, S. M. (2015). On the functions, mechanisms, and malfunctions of intracortical contextual modulation. *Neuroscience and Biobehavioral Review, 52*, 1–20. http://doi.org/10.1016/j.neubiorev.2015.02.010

Pilling, S., Bebbington, P., Kuipers, E., Garety, P., Geddes, J., Orbach, G., & Morgan, C. (2002). Psychological treatments in schizophrenia: I. Meta-analysis of family intervention and cognitive behaviour therapy. *Psychological Medicine, 32*, 763–782. http://doi.org/10.1017/S0033291702005895

Power, B. D., Dragovic, M., Badcock, J. C., Morgan, V. A., Castle, D., Jablensky, A., & Stefanis, N. C. (2015). No additive effect of cannabis on cognition in schizophrenia. *Schizophrenia Research, 168*(1–2), 245–251. http://doi.org/10.1016/j.schres.2015.06.026

Pratt, C., Gill, K., Barrett, N., & Roberts, M. (2014) *Psychiatric rehabilitation* (3rd ed.). New York, NY: Academic Press.

President's New Freedom Commission on Mental Health. (2002). *Final report to the president.* Retrieved from http://govinfo.library.unt.edu/mentalhealthcommission/index.htm

Proenca, C. C., Gao, K. P., Shmelkov, S. V., Rafii, S., & Lee, F. S. (2011). Slitrks as emerging candidate genes involved in neuropsychiatric disorders. *Trends in Neuroscience, 34*, 143–153. http://doi.org/10.1016/j.tins.2011.01.001

Reddy, F., Spaulding, W., Jansen, M., Menditto, A., & Pikett, S. (2010). Psychologists' roles and opportunities in rehabilitation and recovery for serious mental illness: A survey of training and doctoral education. *Training & Education in Professional Psychology, 4*, 254–263. http://doi.org/10.1037/a0021457

Reiser, R. P., Thompson, L. W., Johnson, S. L., & Suppes, T. (2017). *Bipolar Disorder* (2nd ed.). Göttingen, Germany, Boston, MA: Hogrefe.

Roberts, D. L., Combs, D. R., Willoughby, M., Mintz, J., Gibson, C., Rupp, B., & Penn, D. L. (2014). A randomized, controlled trial of Social Cognition and Interaction Training (SCIT) for outpatients with schizophrenia spectrum disorders. *British Journal of Clinical Psychology, 53*(3), 281–298. http://doi.org/10.1111/bjc.12044

Robinson, D. G., Schooler, N. R., John, M., Correll, C. U., Marcy, P., Addington, J., . . . Kane, J. M. (2015). Prescription practices in the treatment of first-episode schizophrenia spectrum disorders: Data from the national RAISE-ETP study. *American Journal of Psychiatry, 172*, 237–248. http://doi.org/10.1176/appi.ajp.2014.13101355

Roder, V., Müller, D. R., Brenner, H. D., & Spaulding, W. D. (2011). *Integrated psychological therapy (IPT) for the treatment of neurocognition, social cognition, and social competency in schizophrenia patients.* Cambridge, MA, Göttingen, Germany: Hogrefe.

Roe, D., Hasson-Ohayon, I., Mashiach-Eizenberg, M., Derhy, O., Lysaker, P. H., & Yanos, P. T. (2014). Narrative enhancement and cognitive therapy (NECT) effectiveness: A quasi-experimental study. *Journal of Clinical Psychology, 70*(4), 303–312. http://doi.org/10.1002/jclp.22050

Rosner, R. I., Lyddon, W. J., & Freeman, A. (2004). Cognitive therapy and dreams: An introduction. In R. I. Rosner, W. J. Lyddon, & A. Freeman (Eds.), *Cognitive therapy and dreams* (pp. 3–8). New York, NY: Springer.

Rossler, W., Ajdacic-Gross, V., Muller, M., Rodgers, S., Haker, H., & Hengartner, M. P. (2015). Assessing sub-clinical psychosis phenotypes in the general population – a multidimensional approach. *Schizophrenia Research, 161*(2–3), 194–201. http://doi.org/10.1016/j.schres.2014.11.033

Salzinger, K. (1973). *Schizophrenia: Behavioral aspects.* New York, NY: John Wiley.

Salzinger, K. (1984). The immediacy hypothesis in a theory of schizophrenia. In W. Spaulding & J. Cole (Eds.), *Theories of schizophrenia and psychosis: The Nebraska Symposium on Motivation* (Vol. 31). Lincoln, NE: University of Nebraska Press.

Sass, L. A., & Parnas, J. (2003). Schizophrenia, consciousness, and the self. *Schizophrenia Bulletin, 29,* 427–444.

Satel, S., & Torrey, E. F. (2016) A prescription for mental health policy. *National Affairs, 27,* 3–22.

Saunders, S. M., & Lueger, R. J. (2005). Evaluation of psychotherapy. In B. J. Sadock & V. A. Sadock (Eds.), *Kaplan & Sadock's comprehensive textbook of psychiatry* (8th ed., pp. 2662–2669). New York, NY: Lippincott, Williams, & Wilkins.

Schwartz, T. L., Sachdeva, S., & Stahl, S. M. (2012). Genetic data supporting the NMDA glutamate receptor hypothesis for schizophrenia. *Current Pharmaceutical Design, 18,* 1580–1592. http://doi.org/10.2174/138161212799958594

Shaner, A., Eckman, T., Roberts, L. J., & Fuller, T. (2003). Feasibility of a skills training approach to reduce substance dependence among individuals with schizophrenia. *Psychiatric Services, 54,* 1287–1289. http://doi.org/10.1176/appi.ps.54.9.1287

Sherman, M. D., Fischer, E., Bowling, U. B., Dixon, L., Ridener, L., & Harrison, D. (2009). A new engagement strategy in a VA-based family psychoeducation program. *Psychiatric Services, 60*(2), 254–257. http://doi.org/10.1176/ps.2009.60.2.254

Silverstein, S. M. (2000). Psychiatric rehabilitation of schizophrenia: Unresolved issues, current trends and future directions. *Applied and Preventive Psychology, 9,* 227–248. http://doi.org/10.1016/S0962-1849(00)80002-5

Silverstein, S. M. (2007). Integrating Jungian and self-psychological perspectives within cognitive-behavior therapy for a young man with a fixed religious delusion. *Clinical Case Studies, 6,* 263–276. http://doi.org/10.1177/1534650106287224

Silverstein, S. M. (2016). Visual perception disturbances in schizophrenia: A unified model. In M. Li & W. Spaulding (Eds.), *The neuropsychopathology of schizophrenia: Molecules, brain systems, motivation and cognition* (pp. 77–132). New York, NY: Springer.

Silverstein, S. M., Del Pozzo, J., Roché, M., Boyle, D. J., & Miskimen, T. (2015). Schizophrenia and violence: Realities and recommendations. *Crime Psychology Review, 1,* 21–42. http://doi.org/10.1080/23744006.2015.1033154

Silverstein, S. M., Hatashita-Wong, M., Wilkniss, S. M., Bloch, A., Smith, T., Savitz, A., . . . Terkelsen, K. (2006). Behavioral rehabilitation of the "treatment-refractory schizophrenia patient: Conceptual foundations, interventions and outcome data. *Psychological Services, 3,* 145–169. http://doi.org/10.1037/1541-1559.3.3.145

Silverstein, S. M., Roché, M. W., Khan, Z., Carson, S. J., Malinovsky, I., Newbill, W. A., . . . Wilkniss, S. M. (2014). Enhancing and promoting recovery In attentionally impaired people diagnosed with schizophrenia: Results from a randomized clinical trial of attention shaping in a partial hospital program. *American Journal of Psychiatric Rehabilitation, 17,* 272–305. http://doi.org/10.1080/15487768.2014.935681

Silverstein, S. M., Spaulding, W., Menditto, A., Savitz, A., Liberman, R., Berten, S., & Starobin, H. (2008). Attention shaping: a reward-based learning method to enhance skills training outcomes in schizophrenia. *Schizophrenia Bulletin, 35,* 222–232. http://doi.org/10.1093/schbul/sbm150

Silverstein, S. M., Wallace, C. J., & Schenkel, L. S. (2005). The Micro-Module Learning Tests: Work sample assessments of responsiveness to skills training interventions. *Schizophrenia Bulletin, 31,* 73–83. http://doi.org/10.1093/schbul/sbi008

Simpson, J. M., & Moriarty, G. L. (2014). *Multimodal treatment of acute psychiatric illness: A guide for hospital diversion.* New York, NY: Columbia University Press.

Smith, A., Li, M., Becker, S., & Kapur, S. (2004). A model of antipsychotic action in conditioned avoidance: a computational approach. *Neuropsychopharmacology, 29,* 1040–1049. http://doi.org/10.1038/sj.npp.1300414

Spaulding, W., Crinean, J., & Martin, T. (1983). Microcomputerized clinical and research laboratories in psychiatric inpatient settings. *Behavior Research Methods and Instrumentation, 15,* 171–176. http://doi.org/10.3758/BF03203542

Spaulding, W. & Deogun, J. (2011). A pathway to personalization of integrated treatment: Informatics and decision science in psychiatric rehabilitation. *Schizophrenia Bulletin, 37*(Suppl. 2), S129–S137. http://doi.org/10.1093/schbul/sbr080

Spaulding, W., Fleming, S. D. R., Sullivan, M., Storzbach, D., & Lam, M. (1999). Cognitive functioning in schizophrenia: Implications for psychiatric rehabilitation. *Schizophrenia Bulletin, 25*(2), 275–289. http://doi.org/10.1093/oxfordjournals.schbul.a033378

Spaulding, W., Johnson, R., Nolting, J., & Collins, A. (2012). Treatment resistant schizophrenia. In D. Castle, T. Copolov, T. Wykes, & K. Mueser (Eds.), *Pharmacological and psychosocial treatment of schizophrenia* (3rd ed.). London, UK: Taylor & Francis.

Spaulding, W., Montague, E., Avila, A. & Sullivan, M. (2016). The idea of recovery. In N. N. Singh, J. W. Barber, & S. Van Sant (Eds.), *Handbook of Recovery in inpatient psychiatry* (pp. 1–36). Berlin, Germany: Springer International.

Spaulding, W., & Nolting, J. (2006). Psychotherapy for schizophrenia in the year 2030: Prognosis and prognostication. *Schizophrenia Bulletin, 32*(Suppl. 1), S94–S105. http://doi.org/10.1093/schbul/sbl024

Spaulding, W., Reed, D., Sullivan, M., Richardson, C., & Weiler, M. (1999). Effects of cognitive treatment in psychiatric rehabilitation. *Schizophrenia Bulletin, 25*, 657–676. http://doi.org/10.1093/oxfordjournals.schbul.a033378

Spaulding, W. & Sullivan, M. (2016a). Cognitive treatment for schizophrenia: The context of psychiatric rehabilitation. *Schizophrenia Bulletin, 42*(Suppl. 1), S53–S61. http://doi.org/10.1093/schbul/sbv163

Spaulding, W. & Sullivan, M. (2016b). Psychotherapy and the schizophrenia spectrum. In L. Beutler, A. Consoli, & B. Bongar (Eds.), *The Oxford comprehensive textbook of psychotherapy* (2nd ed., pp. 378–393). New York, NY: Oxford University Press.

Spaulding, W., Sullivan, M., & Poland, J. (2003). *Treatment and rehabilitation of severe mental illness*. New York, NY: Guilford.

Stahl, S. (2013). *Stahl's essential psychopharmacology: Neuroscientific basis and practical applications* (4th ed.) Cambridge, UK: Cambridge University Press.

Strauss, G., Whearty, K., Frost, K., & Carpenter, W. (2016). An affective neuroscience model of impaired approach motivation in schizophrenia. In M. Li & W. Spaulding (Eds.) *The neuropsychopathology of schizophrenia: Molecules, brain systems, motivation and cognition. Nebraska Symposium on motivation*, Vol. 63 (pp. 159–204). New York, NY: Springer.

Strauss, J., & Carpenter, W. (1977). The treatment of acute schizophrenia without drugs: An investigation of some current assumptions. *American Journal of Psychiatry, 134*, 14–20.

Stuve, P. R., & Menditto, A. A. (1999). State hospitals in the new millennium: Rehabilitating the "not ready for rehab players." In H. R. Lamb (Series Ed.) & W. Spaulding (Vol. Ed.), *New directions for mental health services: No. 84. The state hospital in the 21st century* (pp. 35–46). San Francisco, CA: Jossey-Bass Publishers.

Tarasenko, M., Sullivan, M., Ritchie, A., & Spaulding, W. (2013) The effects of eliminating psychiatric rehabilitation from the secure levels of a psychiatric service system. *Psychological Services, 10*, 442–451. http://doi.org/10.1037/a0030260

Thormodsen, R., Rimol, L. M., Tamnes, C. K., Juuhl-Langseth, M., Holmén, A., Emblem, K. E., . . . Agartz, I. (2013). Age-related cortical thickness differences in adolescents with early-onset schizophrenia compared with healthy adolescents. *Psychiatry Research: Neuroimaging, 214*(3), 190–196. http://doi.org/10.1016/j.pscychresns.2013.07.003

U. S. Department of Human Services. (2004). *National consensus statement on mental health recovery*. Retrieved from http://store.samhsa.gov/shin/content/SMA05-4129/SMA05-4129.pdf

U. S. Government Accountability Office. (2014). *Mental Health: HHS Leadership Needed to Coordinate Federal Efforts Related to Serious Mental Illness.* Retrieved from http://www.gao.gov/assets/670/667644.pdf

van Os, J., & Selten, J.-P. (1998). Prenatal exposure to maternal stress and subsequent schizophrenia: The May 1940 invasion of The Netherlands. *The British Journal of Psychiatry, 172*, 324–326. http://doi.org/10.1192/bjp.172.4.324

Van Rheenen, T. E., Bryce, S., Tan, E. J., Neill, E., Gurvich, C., Louise, S., & Rossell, S. L. (2015). Does cognitive performance map to categorical diagnoses of schizophrenia, schizoaffective disorder and bipolar disorder? A discriminant functions analysis. *Journal of Affective Disorders, 192*, 109–115. http://doi.org/10.1016/j.jad.2015.12.022

Velligan, D. I., Tai, S., Roberts, D. L., Maples-Aguilar, N., Brown, M., Mintz, J., & Turkington, D. (2015). A randomized controlled trial comparing cognitive behavior therapy, cognitive adaptation training, their combination and treatment as usual in chronic schizophrenia. *Schizophrenia Bulletin, 41*(3), 597–603. http://doi.org/10.1093/schbul/sbu127

Walker, E. F. (1994). Developmentally moderated expressions of the neuropathology underlying schizophrenia. *Schizophrenia Bulletin, 20*, 453–480. http://doi.org/10.1093/schbul/20.3.453

Walker, E. F., & Diforio, D. (1997). Schizophrenia: A neural diathesis-stress model. *Psychological Review, 104*, 667–685. http://doi.org/10.1037/0033-295X.104.4.667

Wallace, C. J., Lecomte, T. B., Wilde, M. S., & Liberman, R. P. (2001). A consumer-centered assessment for planning individualized treatment and evaluating program outcomes. *Schizophrenia Research, 66*, 59–70.

Wallace, C. J., Liberman, R. P., MacKain, S. J., Blackwell, G., & Eckman, T. A. (1992). Effectiveness and replicability of modules for teaching social and instrumental skills to the severely mentally ill. *American Journal of Psychiatry, 149*, 654–658.

Wallace, C. J., & Tauber, R. (2004). Supplementing supported employment with workplace skills training. *Psychiatric Services, 55*, 513–515.

Waltereit, R., Banaschewski, T., Meyer-Lindenberg, A., & Poustka, L. (2014). Interaction of neurodevelopmental pathways and synaptic plasticity in mental retardation, autism spectrum disorder and schizophrenia: Implications for psychiatry. *The World Journal of Biological Psychiatry, 15*(7), 507–516. http://doi.org/10.3109/15622975.2013.838641

Walton, E., Liu, J., Hass, J., White, T., Scholz, M., Roessner, V., . . . Ehrlich, S. (2014). MB-COMT promoter DNA methylation is associated with working-memory processing in schizophrenia patients and healthy controls. *Epigenetics, 9*, 1101–1107. http://doi.org/10.4161/epi.29223

Wang, P., Demler, O., & Kessler, R. (2002). Adequacy of treatment for serious mental illness in the United States. *American Journal of Public Health, 92*, 92–98. http://doi.org/10.2105/AJPH.92.1.92

Weisman de Mamani, A., Weintraub, M. J., Gurak, K., & Maura, J. (2014). A randomized clinical trial to test the efficacy of a family-focused, culturally informed therapy for schizophrenia. *Journal of Family Psychology, 28*(6), 800–810. http://doi.org/10.1037/fam0000021

Werbeloff, N., Levine, S. Z., & Rabinowitz, J. (2012). Elaboration on the association between immigration and schizophrenia: A population-based national study disaggregating annual trends, country of origin and sex over 15 years. *Social Psychiatry and Psychiatric Epidemiology, 47*(2), 303–311. http://doi.org/10.1007/s00127-011-0342-3

Wunderink, L., Nieboer, R. M., Wiersma, D., Sytema, S., & Nienhuis, F. J. (2013). Recovery in remitted first-episode psychosis at 7 years of follow-up of an early dose reduction/discontinuation or maintenance treatment strategy: Long-term follow-up of a 2-year randomized clinical trial. *JAMA Psychiatry, 70*(9), 913–920. http://doi.org/10.1001/jamapsychiatry.2013.19

Wykes, T., Huddy, V., Cellard, C., McGurk, S., & Czobor, P. (2011). A meta-analysis of cognitive remediation for schizophrenia: methodology and effect sizes. *American Journal of Psychiatry, 168*, 472–485. http://doi.org/10.1176/appi.ajp.2010.10060855

Wykes, T., & Spaulding, W. (2011). Thinking about the future cognitive remediation therapy – what works and what could we do better? *Schizophrenia Bulletin, 37*(Suppl. 2), S80–S90. http://doi.org/10.1093/schbul/sbr064

Young, A. S., Mintz, J., Cohen, A. N., & Chinman, M. J. (2004). A network-based system to improve care for schizophrenia: The Medical Informatics Network Tool (MINT). *Journal of the American Medical Informatics Association, 11*(5), 358–367. http://doi.org/10.1197/jamia.M1492

8

Appendix: Tools and Resources

I. Government Agencies

National Institute of Mental Health
The NIMH website at http://www.nimh.nih.gov/health/topics/schizophrenia/index.shtml is a portal to basic information about schizophrenia and all the NIMH-sponsored research on the schizophrenia spectrum.

The SAMHSA Store: Publications ordering
The SAMSHA website, at http://store.samhsa.gov, is a portal to all the educational and program development materials produced by the US Substance Abuse and Mental Health Services administration, including the "tool kits" for specific modalities and organizational models described in Section 4 of this book.

II. Professional Organizations

American Psychological Association: Schizophrenia
Informational website at http://apa.org/topics/schiz/index.aspx, with links to information on finding providers and other kinds of help, formatted for consumers and families.

American Psychological Association: Catalog of Clinical Training Opportunities: Best Practices for Recovery and Improved Outcomes for People with Serious Mental Illness
This document was originally developed by the American Psychological Association's Task Force on Serious Mental Illness and updated periodically. The document is intended to assist providers in identifying appropriate interventions for their settings and those they serve, identifying needed advanced clinical training initiatives, and obtaining access to those clinicians and researchers who have developed, implemented, and/or studied the outcomes of the interventions and instruments described. The most recent version can be accessed at http://www.apa.org/practice/resources/grid/catalog.pdf.

American Psychiatric Association: Help With Schizophrenia
Informational website at https://psychiatry.org/patients-families/schizophrenia, with news on recent developments in research and treatment, formatted for consumers and families.

III. Academic Institutions

Boston University: Center for Psychiatric Rehabilitation

A historical center of the psychiatric rehabilitation movement, the Center continues to train psychiatric rehabilitation professionals, develop new modalities, and disseminate information to consumers, professionals, administrators and advocates. The web site at https://cpr.bu.edu is the portal to all their activities and resources.

Dartmouth University: Dartmouth Psychiatric Research Center

A national center for research and development, producing many of the rehabilitation modalities described in Section 4. Their website is at http://dartmouthprc.org.

UCLA: UCLA Center for Neurocognition and Emotion in Schizophrenia

A national research center translating advanced behavioral neuroscience into new approaches to treatment and rehabilitation. Their website is at https://www.semel.ucla.edu/schizophrenia

University of Illinois at Chicago : National Recovery and Training Center on Psychiatric Disability

The NRTC promotes access to consumer-driven and community-based services for adults with serious mental illness, through research on outcomes, online workshops, webcasts, continuing education, and conferences. Their website is at http://www.cmhsrp.uic.edu/nrtc/.

University of Maryland: Maryland Psychiatric Research Center

A research, treatment, and education center focusing on the schizophrenia spectrum, and home of Schizophrenia Bulletin, the leading journal devoted to schizophrenia research. Their website is at http://www.mprc.umaryland.edu.

IV. Advocacy and Interest Organizations

Schizophrenia.com

Schizophrenia.com is a nonprofit web community providing in-depth information, support, and education related to schizophrenia. The website at http://schizophrenia.com offers a wealth of information and links to additional resources.

Mental Health America

Formerly the National Mental Health Association, one of the oldest advocacy organizations in the US for people with schizophrenia spectrum disorders, a collaboration of consumers, families, mental health professionals, and other advocates. Their website is at www.nmha.org

National Alliance for the Mentally Ill (NAMI)

Originally an organization of parents of people with severe mental illness, NAMI membership now includes consumers, family members, mental health professionals and scientists, and other advocates. Their website is at www. nami.org

Schizophrenia Research Forum (SRF)

The SRF contains updates regarding recent research, discussions about new findings, announcements of training webinars, and job postings related to research in schizophrenia. The website is at http://www.schizophreniaforum.org.

V. Foundations, Providers, and Consulting Organizations

Psychiatric Rehabilitation Consultants

A consulting group led by Robert P. Liberman, a pioneer of psychiatric rehabilitation, also disseminating assessment and skill training tools based on those developed by the UCLA Center for Research on Schizophrenia and Psychiatric Rehabilitation. Their web page is at http://www.psychrehab.com

Brain & Behavior Research Foundation

Established in a collaboration of the National Alliance for Mental Illness, the National Mental Health Assocation (Mental Health America) and the National Depressive and Manic Depressive Association, this foundation was previously known as the National Alliance for Research on Schizophrenia and Depression (NARSAD) and continuous to administer a research grant program with that name. Their website is at https://bbrfoundation.org.

Thresholds

The namesake of one of the original psychosocial clubhouse programs, Thresholds is now a multifaceted provider organization with extensive involvement in research, training, and education. Their website is at http://www.thresholds.org.

CET Training, LLC

Organized to produce and disseminate materials for Hogarty et al.'s Cognitive Enhancement Training. Their website is at http://www.cognitiveenhancement therapy.com.

Advances in Psychotherapy

Evidence-Based Practice

Past volumes at a glance:

Vol. 1: Bipolar Disorder *by R. P. Reiser / L. W. Thompson / S. L. Johnson / T. Suppes* **(2nd edition 2017)**
Vol. 2: Heart Disease *by J. A. Skala / K. E. Freedland / R. M. Carney*
Vol. 3: Obsessive-Compulsive Disorder *by J. S. Abramowitz* (out of print, replaced by Vol. 31)
Vol. 4: Childhood Maltreatment *by C. Wekerle / A. L. Miller / D. A. Wolfe / C. B. Spindel*
Vol. 5: The Schizophrenia Spectrum *by W. D. Spaulding / S. M. Silverstein / A. A. Menditto* **(2nd edition 2017)**
Vol. 6: Treating Victims of Mass Disaster and Terrorism *by J. Housley / L. E. Beutler*
Vol. 7: Attention-Deficit/Hyperactivity Disorder in Children and Adults *by A. U. Rickel / R. T. Brown*
(out of print, replaced by Vol. 33 and Vol. 35)
Vol. 8: Problem and Pathological Gambling *by J. P. Whelan / T. A. Steenbergh / A. W. Meyers*
Vol. 9: Chronic Illness in Children and Adolescents *by R. T. Brown / B. P. Daly / A. U. Rickel*
Vol. 10: Alcohol Use Disorders *by S. A. Maisto / G. J. Connors / R. L. Dearing*
Vol. 11: Chronic Pain *by B. J. Field / R. A. Swarm*
Vol. 12: Social Anxiety Disorder *by M. M. Antony / K. Rowa*
Vol. 13: Eating Disorders *by S. W. Touyz / J. Polivy / P. Hay*
Vol. 14: Suicidal Behavior *by R. McKeon*
Vol. 15: Substance Use Problems *by M. Earleywine* **(2nd edition 2016)**
Vol. 16: Elimination Disorders in Children and Adolescents *by E. R. Christophersen / P. C. Friman*
Vol. 17: Sexual Violence *by W. R. Holcomb*
Vol. 18: Depression *by L. P. Rehm*
Vol. 19: Hypochondriasis and Health Anxiety *by J. S. Abramowitz / A. E. Braddock*
Vol. 20: Public Health Tools for Practicing Psychologists *by J. A. Tucker / D. M. Grimley*
Vol. 21: Nicotine and Tobacco Dependence *by A. L. Peterson / M. W. Vander Weg / C. R. Jaén*
Vol. 22: Nonsuicidal Self-Injury *by E. D. Klonsky / J. J. Muehlenkamp / S. P. Lewis / B. Walsh*
Vol. 23: Growing Up with Domestic Violence *by P. G. Jaffe / D. A. Wolfe / M. Campbell*
Vol. 24: Generalized Anxiety Disorder *by C. D. Marker / A. G. Aylward*
Vol. 25: Sexual Dysfunction in Women *by M. Meana*
Vol. 26: Sexual Dysfunction in Men *by D. L. Rowland*
Vol. 27: Phobic and Anxiety Disorders in Children and Adolescents *by A. E. Grills-Taquechel / T. H. Ollendick*
Vol. 28: Language Disorders in Children and Adolescents *by J. H. Beitchman / E. B. Brownlie*
Vol. 29: Autism Spectrum Disorder *by L. Joseph / L. V. Soorya / A. Thurm*
Vol. 30: Headache *by T. A. Smitherman / D. B. Penzien / J. C. Rains / R. A. Nicholson / T. T. Houle*
Vol. 31: Obsessive-Compulsive Disorder in Adults *by J. S. Abramowitz / R. J. Jacoby*
Vol. 32: Binge Drinking and Alcohol Misuse Among College Students and Young Adults *by R. P. Winograd / K. J. Sher*
Vol. 33: Attention-Deficit / Hyperactivity Disorder in Children and Adolescents *by B. P. Daly / A. K. Hildenbrand / R. T. Brown*
Vol. 34: Women and Drinking: Preventing Alcohol-Exposed Pregnancies
by M. M. Velasquez / K. Ingersoll / M. B. Sobell / L. Carter Sobell
Vol. 35: Attention-Deficit / Hyperactivity Disorder in Adults *by B. P. Daly / E. Nicholls / R. T. Brown*
Vol. 36: Multiple Sclerosis *by P. B. Werfel / R. E. Franco Durán / L. J. Trettin*
Vol. 37: Mindfulness *by K. Witkiewitz / C. R. Roos / D. Dharmakaya Colgan / S. Bowen*

Prices: US $29.80 / € 24.95 per volume standing order price US $24.80 / € 19.95 per volume
(minimum 4 successive volumes) + postage & handling. Special rates for APA Division 12 and Division 42 members

www.hogrefe.com

Advances in Psychotherapy

Evidence-Based Practice

Developed and edited with the support of the
Society of Clinical Psychology (APA Division 12)

New Titles

Editors
Danny Wedding, PhD, MPH, USA
Larry E. Beutler, PhD, USA
Kenneth E. Freedland, PhD, USA
Linda Carter Sobell, PhD, ABPP, USA
David. A. Wolfe, PhD, Canada

About the series
The *Advances in Psychotherapy* series provides therapists and students with practical, evidence-based guidance on the diagnosis and treatment of the most common disorders seen in clinical practice – and does so in a uniquely reader-friendly manner. Each book is both a compact "how-to" reference on a particular disorder, for use by professional clinicians in their daily work, and an ideal educational resource for students and for practice-oriented continuing education. The books all have a similar structure, and each title is a compact and easy-to-follow guide covering all aspects of practice that are relevant in real life. Tables, boxed clinical "pearls," and marginal notes assist orientation, while checklists for copying and summary boxes provide tools for use in daily practice.

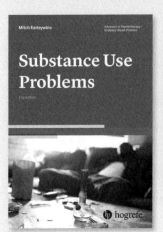

Volume 15
2nd ed. 2016, viii + 104 pp.
ISBN 978-0-88937-416-4

Volume 1
2nd ed. 2017, viii + 120 pp.
ISBN 978-0-88937-410-2

Volume 37
2017, viii + 80 pp.
ISBN 978-0-88937-414-0

hogrefe